MY KIND
OF VERSE

MY KIND OF VERSE

COMPILED BY
JOHN SMITH

DECORATIONS BY URI SHULEVITZ

THE MACMILLAN COMPANY, NEW YORK

Library of Congress catalog card number: 68-20609
Printed in the United States of America
FIRST PRINTING

ACKNOWLEDGMENTS

Thanks are due to the following poets, agents and publishers for permission to reprint poems in this anthology:

Dannie Abse for "Albert" and "Song of a Hebrew."

Gene Baro for "The Ferns."

Taner Baybars for "Waves Against a Dog."

John Buxton and Macmillan & Co. Ltd. for "Harebell" by John Buxton (from *Such Liberty*).

Jonathan Cape Ltd. for "Stuff" and "The Elephant Knocked the Ground" by Adrian Mitchell.

Charles Causley for "Timothy Winters", published by Rupert Hart-Davis.

Richard Church for "Mirage" (from *Collected Poems of Richard Church*), published by William Heinemann Ltd.

Leonard Clark for "Revelation."

Simon Cohen for "Reunion in Kensington."

Constable Publishers for "Gay Comes the Singer," translated by Helen Waddell (from *Medieval Latin Lyrics*).

The Cresset Press for "To a Fat Lady Seen from the Train" by Frances Cornford (from *Collected Poems*), "The Weed" (from *The Rude Potato*) and "For Sleep, or Death" (from *Urania*) by Ruth Pitter; "The Boy Fishing" by E. J. Scovell (from *The River Steamer*).

André Deutsch, Ltd. for "Nipping Pussy's Feet in Fun" and "My Hat" by Stevie Smith.

Doubleday & Company, Inc. for "The Bat" by Theodore Roethke (from *The Collected Poems of Theodore Roethke*), Copyright 1938 by Theodore Roethke.

Gerald Duckworth & Co., Ltd. for "In the Fields" by Charlotte Mew; "Milk for the Cat" by Harold Monro.

1964 by Philip Larkin; "Words" by Stephen Spender (from *Collected Poems 1928–1953*), Copyright 1948 by Stephen Spender, originally appeared in *The New Yorker*.

Jeremy Robson for "Fragment" from *33 Poems*, published by Sidgwick & Jackson.

Paul Roche for "Morning Glory."

Routledge & Kegan Paul Ltd. for "Autumn" by T. E. Hulme.

Anthony Rye for "Birds Must Sing."

Siegfried Sassoon for "Everyone Sang."

Vernon Scannell for "First Fight."

William R. Scott, Inc., for "I Am Rose" by Gertrude Stein (from *The World Is Round*), Copyright renewed 1967 by Daniel C. Joseph Admr. d.b.n. CTA of The Estate of Gertrude Stein.

Charles Scribner's Sons for "I Too! I Too!" by John Hall Wheelock from *Poems 1911–1936* by John Hall Wheelock, Copyright 1936 by Charles Scribner's Sons.

Jean Murray Simpson for "Spring Song."

John Smith for "A True Story," "Look!" "I Am Tired of the Wind."

Odette Tchernine for "The Gnats."

Sydney Tremayne for "Slow Spring."

Wesleyan University Press for "Happy Wind," "Leisure," and "The Bird-Man" by W. H. Davies from *The Complete Poems of W. H. Davies*, Copyright © 1963 by Jonathan Cape Ltd.

Ann Wolfe for "Green Candles" and "Two Sparrows" by Humbert Wolfe.

CONTENTS

Introduction   XV

SONGS AND SIMPLES

MAGIC AND MYSTERY

TALL TALES

ODD BODS

PLACES, WEATHERS, CREATURES, THINGS

STUFF AND NONSENSE

WISDOMS, PRAISE, PRAYERS AND GRACES

INTRODUCTION

Living, as we do, at a time when almost every day confronts us with some new example of man's ingenuity—the possibility of landing a man on the moon, a miraculous heart operation, an astonishing development in the biological field, the manufacture of some hitherto undreamed-of material—we are sometimes inclined to doubt the value of the arts and, especially, of the art of poetry. What is it for? What good is it? What does it do? It is easy enough to shrug these questions off with a "nothing very much" but if we do this then we have to ask another question: "If poetry is not useful, why do people persist in writing it and why do people still need to read it?" The answer is, of course, that like music, painting, sculpture, indeed, all man's endeavor in the various fields of art, poetry reveals truths and realities that lie deeper than those exhibited by most of man's working activities. Poetry helps to show us what we are, what the world is all about. By the vividness of its language it can help to show us features of the world that had hitherto escaped our notice; by its insight into our emotions it can, often in the most subtle way, modify our whole being; by its rhythms it can at times transport us beyond the mundane pace of our daily living; by its wisdom it can bring us closer to an apprehension of the great mysteries of the universe.

Mostly these questions about "what is the use of poetry" are asked by adults. Children are wiser. It is easier for them to accept things for what they are and undoubtedly most young children respond readily to poetry. They see the world through eyes which have not yet been clouded by the strictures of social convention or departmentalized into a hundred and one areas of particular knowledge. The world of fantasy and actuality are close; the conditions of joy and sadness divided by the narrowest gulf. They often, and very startlingly, put our adult reasoning to shame. A young English poet, Jeremy Robson, has put this very neatly in his poem entitled "Fragment":

> He watched with fascination
> the rain
> pouring on our generation
> and the clumsy plumbers
> struggling to plug the holes.
> As the holes broadened
> pencils scribbled on paper
> sums were done
> wars were won,
> the minister cleared his throat
> glanced at his notes
> began to chant his speech:
> "Twice two are four"
> he said,
> but the child smiled in disbelief
> facts (he knew) were never true.

Although the present anthology is divided into sections, the first of which happens to be entitled *Songs and Simples*, it must not be thought that the poems get more difficult as the book goes on. The readers at whom this collection is aimed encompass enormous differences in emotional and intellectual understanding. There are some poems here which at first sight may seem far too mature for the older children and some which may seem too young even for the kindergarten. But many young children are immensely sophisticated and they must at all costs be allowed to stretch their minds and imagination at this very significant age. A child who can appreciate many of the wonders of the "space age" is not going to be healthfully fed by a constant diet of nonexistent fairies at the bottom of more or less nonexistent gardens. On the other hand some modern tendencies are so extreme as to suppose that violence both in behavior and art is to be desired and portrayed and that anything "beautiful" is immediately suspect. I hope we never grow too ancient or clever to delight in such lines and sentiments as "And what will the robin do then? Poor thing."

Another problem that bedevils the appreciation of poetry is the belief that it is something hallowed. This "holier than thou" attitude needs to be swept away, together with the kind of unctuous poetry voice that goes with it. I hope the poems in this book, and their juxtaposition, will help to let a little light and air into what is so often one of the dustiest lessons endured in schools.

There are relatively few "children's poems" included in this selection. My first principle in choosing the poems has not been to ask, "Is this a suitable poem for a child?" but rather, "Do *I* like this poem?" Only if the answer has been "yes" have I then put the supplementary question about suitability. I make no pretense of liking all these poems equally, but each has something about it—some interesting thought, some verbal felicity, some neatness of expression, perhaps one ingenious line—that appeals to me. Sometimes it is a surrealist extravagance of humor as in "A Reunion in Kensington," or the outrageous puns in "Mary's

Ghost," the tender throwaway modernity of Paul Lewenstein's little "Adieu," the neat placing of the word *and* in "A Fox Rhyme." Serious, comic, tender or harsh, I hope no one will think these poems dull.

Although there are many first-class poems in this book, it obviously does not attempt to include very many of the great masterpieces of the language; those poems with their profound delights and modifying influences can only be appreciated when the door into their world has been opened. I hope the poems in this anthology will help to push that door wide.

For the most part the poems included here are fairly short. Many are indeed only a few lines. But there is one section devoted to longer poems. It is in this part of the anthology that the greatest difficulty may seem to lie. But I believe many readers will welcome one or two poems with a story line, such as Vernon Scannell's "First Fight," and that many will delight in the irreverence and the slangy tone of Ruth Pitter's satirical poem "The Weed," and will respond to the moral fable of Auden's "James Honeyman." Many of the poems in this section, especially "The Daniel Jazz," are excellent for choral speaking either in part or in whole.

I have tried to avoid poems that have a complicated structure or a wealth of allusion, but where a poem has a specific reference that may not be immediately understood I have added a note at the end of the book; I have kept such notes to a minimum.

Among the poems in this anthology is one by Adrian Mitchell which has the constant refrain: *I like that stuff.* I had originally thought of using that line as the title of the book but decided that it was not perhaps sufficiently indicative of the fact that the book is a collection of poems. Nevertheless, I hope the line will be constantly in the mind of the reader, whether child or adult, when reading the contents. Poetry is something to be enjoyed, yet how often do we hear adults saying: "Oh, poetry! I can't stand it. I remember having to learn it at school!" What a devastating indictment that is of some of our educational methods: one of the supreme achievements of the English-speaking world reduced to a drudge and a chore. I hope that the poems in this collection will help to remove this attitude; that teachers and children alike will read them, because they are enjoyable, moving, sad or jolly, and not study them out of a dreary sense of duty.

John Smith

SONGS AND
SIMPLES

THE NORTH WIND DOTH BLOW

The north wind doth blow
And we shall have snow,
And what will the robin do then?
    Poor thing.
He'll sit in a barn
And keep himself warm,
And hide his head under his wing,
    Poor thing.

NURSERY RHYME

HAREBELL

Harebell! Harebell!
If I shall send
The wind to swing
Your delicate stem—
When the war end
Will you ring? Will you ring?

Listen! Listen!
My bells all peal
Even now. I know
No joy but the sun
And the wind that I feel
As it blows to and fro.

JOHN BUXTON

PIRATE

Like a cliff
My brow hangs over
The cave of my eyes
My nose is the prow of a ship
I plunder the world

SAMUEL MENASHE

O DEAR ME!

Here are crocuses, white, gold, grey!
   "O dear me!" says Marjorie May;
Flat as a platter the blackberry blows:
   "O dear me!" says Madeleine Rose;
The leaves are fallen, the swallows flown:
   "O dear me!" says Humphrey John;
Snow lies thick where all night it fell:
   "O dear me!" says Emanuel.

WALTER DE LA MARE

LOOK!

I eat from the dish of the world
   Trees, fields, flowers.
I drink from the glass of space
   Blue sea, sky.

I pour the sky over me
   In blue showers.
Look! I light up the day
   With my eye.

JOHN SMITH

PUSSY AT THE FIRESIDE

Pussy at the fireside
Suppin' pease brose:
Down came a cinder
And burnt pussy's nose.

"Oh," said Pussy
"That's no fair!"
"Oh," said the cinder,
"You shouldnie been there!"

CHILDREN'S RHYME

TO BLOSSOMS

Fair pledges of a fruitful tree,
   Why do ye fall so fast?
   Your date is not so past,
But you may stay yet here awhile,
   To blush and gently smile
      And go at last.

What, were ye born to be
   An hour or half's delight,
   And so to bid good-night?
'Twas pity Nature brought ye forth
   Merely to show your worth,
      And lose you quite.

But you are lovely leaves, where we
   May read how soon things have
   Their end, though ne'er so brave:
And after they have shown their pride
   Like you awhile, they glide
      Into the grave.

ROBERT HERRICK

TO THE MOON

Art thou pale for weariness
Of climbing heaven, and gazing on the earth,
Wandering companionless
Among the stars that have a different birth,—
And ever-changing, like a joyless eye
That finds no object worth its constancy?

PERCY BYSSHE SHELLEY

HAPPY WIND

O, happy wind, how sweet
Thy life must be!
The great, proud fields of gold
Run after thee:
And here are flowers, with heads
To nod and shake;
And dreaming butterflies
To tease and wake,
Oh, happy wind, I say,
To be alive this day.

W. H. DAVIES

I HAD A LITTLE NUT TREE

I had a little nut tree,
   Nothing would it bear
But a silver nutmeg
   And a golden pear;

The King of Spain's daughter
   Came to visit me,
And all for the sake
   Of my little nut tree.

NURSERY RHYME

LADYBIRD, LADYBIRD

Ladybird, Ladybird,
   Fly away home,
Your house is on fire
And your children are gone;
All except one
   And that's little Ann
And she has crept under
   The warming pan.

NURSERY RHYME

TO AN ISLE IN THE WATER

Shy one, shy one,
Shy one of my heart,
She moves in the firelight
Pensively apart.

She carries in the dishes,
And lays them in a row.
To an isle in the water
With her would I go.

She carries in the candles,
And lights the curtained room,
Shy in the doorway
And shy in the gloom;

And shy as a rabbit,
Helpful and shy.
To an isle in the water
With her would I fly.

W. B. YEATS

CHILD'S SONG

I have a garden of my own,
   Shining with flowers of every hue;
I loved it dearly while alone,
   But I shall love it more with you:
And there the golden bees shall come,
   In summer time at break of morn,
And wake us with their busy hum
   Around the Siha's fragrant thorn.

I have a fawn from Aden's land,
   On leafy buds and berries nursed;
And you shall feed him from your hand,
   Though he may start with fear at first;
And I will lead you where he lies
   For shelter in the noon-tide heat;
And you may touch his sleeping eyes,
   And feel his little silvery feet.

THOMAS MOORE

WHEN I WAS A LITTLE GIRL

When I was a little girl,
   About seven years old,
I hadn't got a petticoat,
   To keep me from the cold.

So I went into Darlington,
   That pretty little town,
And there I bought a petticoat,
   A cloak and a gown,

I went into the woods
   And built me a kirk,
And all the birds of the air,
   They helped me to work.

The hawk, with his long claws,
   Pulled down the stone,
The dove, with her rough bill,
   Brought me them home.

The parrot was the clergyman,
   The peacock was the clerk,
The bullfinch played the organ,
   And we made merry work.

         NURSERY RHYME

NIPPING PUSSY'S FEET IN FUN

Oh Mr. Pussy-cat,
My, you are sweet!
How do you get about so much
On those tiny feet?
Nip, nip; miaou, miaou,
Tiny little feet,
Nip, nip, pussy-cat
My, you are sweet!

STEVIE SMITH

THE HORSEMAN

I heard a horseman
　Ride over the hill;
The moon shone clear,
The night was still;
His helm was silver,
　And pale was he;
And the horse he rode
　Was of ivory.

WALTER DE LA MARE

from *SUNDAY AT HAMPSTEAD*

As we rush, as we rush in the Train,
   The trees and the houses go wheeling back,
But the starry heavens above the plain
   Come flying on our track.

All the beautiful stars of the sky
   The silver doves of the forest of Night,
Over the dull earth swarm and fly,
   Companions of our flight.

We will rush ever on without fear;
   Let the goal be far, the flight be fleet!
For we carry the Heavens with us, Dear,
   While the earth slips from our feet.

JAMES THOMSON (B.V.)

AUTUMN

A touch of cold in the autumn night—
I walked abroad,
And saw the ruddy moon lean over a hedge
Like a red-faced farmer.
I did not stop to speak, but nodded,
And round about were the wistful stars
With white faces like town children.

                    T. E. HULME

THE TIDE IN THE RIVER

The tide in the river,
The tide in the river,
The tide in the river runs deep,
I saw a shiver
Pass over the river
As the tide turned in its sleep.

            ELEANOR FARJEON

Introduction to
SONGS OF INNOCENCE

Piping down the valleys wild,
Piping songs of pleasant glee,
On a cloud I saw a child,
And he laughing said to me:

"Pipe a song about a Lamb!"
So I piped with merry cheer.
"Piper, pipe that song again;"
So I piped: he wept to hear.

"Drop thy pipe, thy happy pipe;
Sing thy songs of happy cheer;"
So I sang the same again,
While he wept with joy to hear.

"Piper, sit thee down and write
In a book, that all may read."
So he vanished from my sight,
And I plucked a hollow reed,

And I made a rural pen,
And I stained the water clear,
And I wrote my happy songs
Every child may joy to hear.

WILLIAM BLAKE

AN AMULET

A-
round
my neck
an amu-
let
Be-
tween
my eyes
a star
A
ring
in my
nose
and a
gold
chain
to
Keep me
where
you
are

SAMUEL MENASHE

15

Song from *CHARLES IV*

A widow bird sate mourning for her love
   Upon a wintry bough;
The frozen wind crept on above,
   The freezing stream below.

There was no leaf upon the forest bare,
   No flower upon the ground,
And little motion in the air
   Except the mill-wheel's sound.

PERCY BYSSHE SHELLEY

A FLOCK OF LITTLE BOATS

A flock of little boats
Tethered to the shore
Drifts in still water. . . .
Prows dip, nibbling.

   SAMUEL MENASHE

CAST OUR CAPS AND CARES AWAY

Cast our caps and cares away:
This is beggar's holiday!
At the crowning of our king,
Thus we ever dance and sing.
In the world look out and see,
Where so happy a prince as he?
Where the nation lives so free,
And so merry as do we?
Here at liberty we are,
And enjoy our ease and rest:
To the field we are not pressed;
Nor are called into the town,
To be troubled with the gown.
Hang all offices, we cry,
And the magistrate too, by!
When the subsidy's increased,
We are not a penny sessed;
Nor will any go to law
With the beggar for a straw.
All which happiness, he brags,
He doth owe unto his rags.

JOHN FLETCHER

ONE TWO THREE

One, two, three, four, five,
Once I caught a fish alive,
Six, seven, eight, nine, ten,
Then I let it go again.

Why did you let it go?
Because it bit my finger so.
Which finger did it bite?
This little finger on the right.

NURSERY RHYME

I AM ROSE

I am Rose my eyes are blue
I am Rose and who are you?
I am Rose and when I sing
I am Rose like anything.

GERTRUDE STEIN

SING A SONG OF SIXPENCE

Sing a song of sixpence,
   A pocket full of rye;
Four and twenty blackbirds,
   Baked in a pie.

When the pie was opened,
   The birds began to sing;
Was not that a dainty dish
   To set before the king?

The king was in his counting-house,
   Counting out his money;
The queen was in the parlor,
   Eating bread and honey.

The maid was in the garden,
   Hanging out the clothes,
There came a little blackbird
   And snapped off her nose.

NURSERY RHYME

UPON HER FEET

Her pretty feet
Like snails did creep
A little out, and then,
As if they started at bo-peep
Did soon draw in again.

ROBERT HERRICK

THE LILY

The modest Rose puts forth a thorn,
The humble Sheep a threatening horn;
While the Lily white shall in Love delight,
Nor a thorn, nor a threat, stain her beauty bright.

WILLIAM BLAKE

SPIDER WEBS

Spider webs are very delicate
And to remember.

A spider web is sometimes breaking.
It breaks when you take it
Or where it shakes in the wind
But always to remember
And delicate.

Delicate is when a thing is breaking
Sometimes when you take it
Or in the wind when it shakes.

Spider webs are to remember
That things are delicate and sometimes break.
But after they break
You remember.

RAY FABRIZIO

HARK, HARK! THE LARK

Hark, hark! The Lark at heaven's gate sings
   And Phoebus 'gins arise,
His steeds to water at those springs
   On chaliced flowers that lies;
And winking Mary-buds begin
   To ope their golden eyes;
With every thing that pretty is,
   My lady, sweet, arise:
      Arise, arise!

WILLIAM SHAKESPEARE
(*from* Cymbeline)

THREE JOVIAL HUNTSMEN

There were three jovial huntsmen,
  As I have heard them say,
And they would go a-hunting
  All on a summer's day.

All day they hunted,
  And nothing could they find
But a ship a-sailing,
  A-sailing with the wind.

One said it was a ship,
  The other said Nay;
The third said it was a house
  With the chimney blown away.

And all night they hunted,
  And nothing could they find;
But the moon a-gliding,
  A-gliding with the wind.

One said it was the moon,
  The other said Nay;
The third said it was a cheese,
  And half of it cut away.

                              ANON

A GIRL

The tree has entered my hands,
The sap has ascended my arms,
The tree has grown in my breast—
Downward,
The branches grow out of me, like arms.

Tree you are,
Moss you are,
You are violets with the wind above them.
A child—*so* high—you are,
And all this is folly to the world.

EZRA POUND

THE TIRED MAN

I am a quiet gentleman,
And I would sit and dream;
But my wife is on the hillside,
Wild as a hill stream.

I am a quiet gentleman,
And I would sit and think;
But my wife is walking the whirlwind
Through night as black as ink.

O, give me a woman of my race
As well controlled as I,
And let us sit by the fire,
Patient till we die!

ANNA WICKHAM

PLOUGHING ON SUNDAY

The white cock's tail
Tosses in the wind.
The turkey-cock's tail
Glitters in the sun.

Water in the fields.
The wind pours down.
The feathers flare
And bluster in the wind.

Remus, blow your horn!
I'm ploughing on Sunday,
Ploughing North America.
Blow your horn!

Tum-ti-tum,
Ti-tum-tum-tum!
The turkey-cock's tail
Spreads to the sun.

The white cock's tail
Streams in the moon.
Water in the fields.
The wind pours down.

WALLACE STEVENS

QUEEN NEFERTITI

Spin a coin, spin a coin,
  All fall down;
Queen Nefertiti
  Stalks through the town.

Over the pavements
  Her feet go clack
Her legs are as tall
  As a chimney stack;

Her fingers flicker
  Like snakes in the air,
The walls split open
  At her green-eyed stare;

Her voice is thin
  As the ghosts of bees;
She will crumble your bones,
  She will make your blood freeze.

Spin a coin, spin a coin,
  All fall down;
Queen Nefertiti
  Stalks through the town.

ANON

I HAD A BOAT

I had a boat and the boat had wings;
   And I did dream that we went a-flying
Over the heads of queens and kings,
   Over the souls of dead and dying,
Up among the stars and the great white rings,
   And where the moon on her back is lying.

MARY COLERIDGE

THE SONG OF WANDERING AENGUS

I went out to the hazel wood,
Because a fire was in my head,
And cut and peeled a hazel wand
And hooked a berry to a thread;
And when white moths were on the wing,
And moth-like stars were flickering out,
I dropped the berry in a stream
And caught a little silver trout.

When I had laid it on the floor
I went to blow the fire aflame,
But something rustled on the floor
And someone called me by my name:
It had become a glimmering girl
With apple blossom in her hair
Who called me by my name and ran
And faded through the brightening air.

Though I am old with wandering
Through hollow lands and hilly lands
I will find out where she has gone,
And kiss her lips and take her hands;
And walk among long dappled grass,
And pluck till time and times are done
The silver apples of the moon,
The golden apples of the sun.

W. B. YEATS

MIRAGE

I saw a man on a horse
Riding against the sun.
"Hallo, Don Cossack!" I cried.
He shouted, "Hallo, my son!"

The Caspian sea shimmered:
The Kazak tents shone
For a moment in England,
Then the horseman was gone.

RICHARD CHURCH

IN MARBLE HALLS

In marble halls as white as milk,
Lined with skin as soft as silk,
Within a fountain crystal-clear,
A golden apple doth appear.
No doors there are to this stronghold,
Yet thieves break in and steal the gold.

NURSERY RHYME

I, TOO! I, TOO!

Wild geese, wild geese, arrowing down the sky,
　　Hastening, hastening, where the heavens are bare!
I, too, would flee away—I know not why;
　　I, too, would hasten—but I know not where!

JOHN HALL WHEELOCK

WHERE THE BEE SUCKS

Where the bee sucks, there suck I:
In a cowslip's bell I lie;
There I couch when owls do cry.
On the bat's back I do fly
After summer merrily.
Merrily, merrily shall I live now
Under the blossom that hangs on the bough.

WILLIAM SHAKESPEARE
(*from* The Tempest)

GREEN CANDLES

"There's someone at the door," said gold candlestick:
"Let her in quick, let her in quick!"
"There is a small hand groping at the handle:
Why don't you turn it?" asked green candle.

"Don't go, don't go," said the Hepplewhite chair,
"Lest you find a strange lady there."
"Yes, stay where you are," whispered the white wall:
"There is nobody there at all."

"I know her little foot," grey carpet said:
"Who but I should know her light tread?"
"She shall come in," answered the open door,
"And not," said the room, "go out any more."

HUMBERT WOLFE

SONG

Ye spotted snakes with double tongue,
  Thorny hedgehogs, be not seen;
Newts and blindworms, do no wrong,
  Come not near our fairy Queen.

Weaving spiders, come not here;
  Hence, you long-legged spinners, hence!
Beetles black, approach not near;
  Worm nor snail do no offence.

    Philomel, with melody
   Sing in our sweet lullaby;
Lulla, lulla, lullaby; lulla, lulla; lullaby;
     Never harm,
    Nor spell, nor charm,
 Come our lovely Lady nigh;
So goodnight, with lullaby.

WILLIAM SHAKESPEARE
(*from* A Midsummer Night's Dream)

THERE WAS A MAN

There was a man of double deed
Sowed his garden full of seed.
When the seed began to grow,
'Twas like a garden full of snow;
When the snow began to melt,
'Twas like a ship without a belt;
When the ship began to sail,
'Twas like a bird without a tail;
When the bird began to fly,
'Twas like an eagle in the sky;
When the sky began to roar,
'Twas like a lion at the door;
When the door began to crack,
'Twas like a stick across my back;
When my back began to smart,
'Twas like a penknife in my heart;
When my heart began to bleed,
'Twas death and death and death indeed.

NURSERY RHYME

THE FALCON

Lully, Lulley! Lully, Lulley!
The falcon hath borne my make away!

He bare him up, he bare him down,
He bare him into an orchard brown.

In that orchard there was an hall,
That was hangéd with purple and pall.

And in that hall there was a bed,
It was hangéd with gold so red.

And in that bed there lieth a knight,
His woundës bleeding day and night.

At that bed's foot there lieth a hound,
Licking the blood as it runs down.

By that bedside there kneeleth a may,
And she weepeth both night and day.

And at that bed's head there standeth a stone,
Corpus Christi written thereon.

Lully, Lulley! Lully, Lulley!
The falcon hath borne my make away.

ANON

FULL FATHOM FIVE

Full fathom five thy father lies;
   Of his bones are coral made;
Those are pearls that were his eyes:
   Nothing of him that doth fade,
But doth suffer a sea-change
Into something rich and strange.
Sea-nymphs hourly ring his knell:
       Ding-dong.
Hark! now I hear them—ding-dong, bell.

WILLIAM SHAKESPEARE
(*from* The Tempest)

THE KNIFESMITH

I am the man who made the knife
  That killed the king of Babylon;
It had a sheath of beaten gold,
  And in its haft strange jewels shone.

I wrought it through the winter days,
  And when they brightened into spring
I led it to the light, and knew
  It was a dagger for a king.

I sent it humbly to the king,
  As being fit for him to wear;
His page-boy brought it back to me:
  "The king has daggers and to spare."

But while I dozed beside my fire,
  Beside my fire, as night drew on,
A hand came rustling through the wall
  And seized the dagger and was gone.

Next morning when the king was dead,
  And princes snarling in his hall,
The dagger he had scorned to wear
  Was back upon my workshop wall.

And seeing it upon my wall,
    And knowing that the king was dead,
How could I turn to making knives
    For chopping meat or cutting bread?

No, I shall wear it at my side,
    And wander through the world, until
On some auspicious night, we find
    Another king for it to kill.

DOROTHY HOWARD

A MEETING

When George began to climb all unawares
He saw a horrible face at the top of the stairs.

The rats came tumbling down the planks,
Pushing past without a word of thanks.

The rats were thin, the stairs were tall,
But the face at the top was the worst of all.

It wasn't the ghost of his father or mother.
When they are laid there's always another.

It wasn't the ghost of people he knew.
It was worse than this, shall I tell you who?

It was himself, oh what a disgrace.
And soon they were standing face to face.

At first they pretended neither cared,
But when they met they stood and stared.

One started to smile and the other to frown,
And one moved up and the other moved down.

But which emerged and which one stays,
Nobody will know till the end of his days.

GEORGE D. PAINTER
(*from* Encounters with a Doppelganger)

THE SONG OF THE MAD PRINCE

Who said, "Peacock Pie"?
    The old King to the sparrow:
Who said, "Crops are ripe"?
    Rust to the harrow:
Who said, "Where sleeps she now?
    Where rests she now her head,
Bathed in Eve's loveliness"?—
    That's what I said.

Who said, "Ay, mum's the word"?
    Sexton to willow:
Who said, "Green dusk for dreams,
    Moss for a pillow"?
Who said, "All Time's delight
    Hath she for narrow bed;
Life's troubled bubble broken"?
    That's what I said.

WALTER DE LA MARE

THE QUEEN OF FAIRIES

Come follow, follow me,
You, fairy elves that be,
Which circle on the green;
Come follow me, your queen.
  Hand in hand, let's dance a round,
  For this place is fairy ground.

When mortals are at rest,
And snoring in their nest;
Unheard and unespied,
Through keyholes we do glide;
  Over tables, stools and shelves,
  We trip it with our fairy elves.

And, if the house be foul,
Or platter, dish, or bowl,
Upstairs we nimbly creep,
And find the sluts asleep:
  There we pinch their arms and thighs—
  None escapes; nor none espies.

But if the house be swept,
And from uncleanness kept,
We praise the household maid,
And surely she is paid:
  For we do use before we go
  To drop a tester in her shoe.

Upon a mushroom's head,
Our table we do spread;
A grain of rye, or wheat,

Is manchet, which we eat;
    Pearly drops of dew we drink
    In acorn cups to fill the brink.

The brains of nightingales,
With unctuous dew of snails,
Between two nutshells stewed,
Is meat that's easily chewed;
    And the beards of little mice
    Do make a feast of wondrous price.

On tops of dewy grass,
So nimbly do we pass,
The young and tender stalk
Ne'er bends where we do walk;
    Yet in the morning may be seen
    Where we, the night before, have been.

The grasshopper, gnat and fly,
Serve for our minstrelsy;
Grace said, we dance a while,
And so the time beguile:
    And when the moon doth hide her head,
    The glow-worm lights us home to bed.

ANON

NOW THE HUNGRY LION ROARS

Now the hungry lion roars
   And the wolf behowls the moon:
Whilst the heavy ploughman snores,
   All with weary task fordone.
Now the wasted brands do glow,
   Whilst the screech-owl, screeching loud,
Puts the wretch that lies in woe
   In remembrance of a shroud.
Now it is the time of night,
   That the graves, all gaping wide,
Every one lets forth his sprite,
   In the churchway paths to glide:
And we fairies, that do run
   By the triple Hecate's team,
From the presence of the sun,
   Following darkness like a dream,
Now are frolic: not a mouse
Shall disturb this hallowed house:
I am sent with broom before,
To sweep the dust behind the door.

WILLIAM SHAKESPEARE
(*from* A Midsummer Night's Dream)

THE GHOSTS

In life three ghostly friars were we,
And now three friarly ghosts we be.
Around our shadowy table placed,
The spectral bowl before us floats;
With wine that none but ghosts can taste,
We wash our unsubstantial throats.
Three merry ghosts—three merry ghosts—three merry
    ghosts are we:
Let the ocean be Port, and we'll think it good sport
To be laid in that Red Sea.

With songs that jovial spectres chaunt,
Our old refectory still we haunt.
The traveller hears our midnight mirth:
"O list!" he cries, "the haunted choir!
The merriest ghost that walks the earth,
Is sure the ghost of a ghostly friar."
Three merry ghosts—three merry ghosts—three merry
    ghosts are we:
Let the ocean be Port, and we'll think it good sport
To be laid in that Red Sea.

THOMAS LOVE PEACOCK

LA BELLE DAME SANS MERCI

O what can ail thee, knight-at-arms,
　　Alone and palely loitering?
The sedge is withered from the lake,
　　And no birds sing.

O what can ail thee, knight-at-arms,
　　So haggard and so woe-begone?
The squirrel's granary is full,
　　And the harvest's done.

I see a lily on thy brow
　　With anguish moist and fever dew,
And on thy cheek a fading rose
　　Fast withereth too.

I met a lady in the meads,
　　Full beautiful—a faery's child,
Her hair was long, her foot was light,
　　And her eyes were wild.

I made a garland for her head,
　　And bracelets too, and fragrant zone,
She looked at me as she did love
　　And made sweet moan.

I set her on my pacing steed,
　　And nothing else saw all day long,
For sideways would she lean, and sing
　　A faery's song.

She found me roots of relish sweet,
　　And honey wild, and manna dew,

And sure in language strange she said—
  "I love thee true!"

She took me to her elfin grot,
  And there she wept and sighed full sore,
And there I shut her wild, wild eyes
  With kisses four.

And there she lulléd me asleep,
  And there I dreamed—ah, woe betide!
The latest dream I ever dreamed
  On the cold hill's side.

I saw pale kings and princes too,
  Pale warriors, death-pale were they all;
They cried—"La Belle Dame sans Merci
  Hath thee in thrall!"

I saw their starved lips in the gloom,
  With horrid warning gaped wide,
And I awoke and found me here,
  On the cold hill's side.

And this is why I sojourn here,
  Alone and palely loitering,
Though the sedge is withered from the lake,
  And no birds sing.

JOHN KEATS

THE HAG

The Hag is astride,
This night for to ride;
The Devil and she together:
Through thick and through thin,
Now out and then in,
Though ne'er so foul be the weather.

A thorn or a burr
She takes for a spur:
With a lash of a bramble she rides now,
Through brakes and through briars,
O'er ditches and mires,
She follows the Spirit that guides now.

No Beast, for his food,
Dares now range the wood;
But hushed in his lair he lies lurking:
While mischiefs, by these,
On land and on seas,
At noon of night are a-working.

The storm will arise
And trouble the skies;
This night, and more for the wonder,
The ghost from the tomb
Affrighted shall come,
Called out by the clap of the thunder.

ROBERT HERRICK

PEGASUS

From the blood of Medusa
Pegasus sprang.
His hoof of heaven
Like melody rang.
His whinny was sweeter
Than Orpheus' lyre,
The wing on his shoulder
Was brighter than fire.

His tail was a fountain,
His nostrils were caves,
His mane and his forelock
Were musical waves,
He neighed like a trumpet,
He cooed like a dove,
He was stronger than terror
And swifter than love.

He could not be captured,
He could not be bought,
His rhythm was running,
His standing was thought.
With one eye on sorrow
And one eye on mirth
He galloped in heaven
And gambolled on earth.

And only the poet
With wings to his brain

Can mount him and ride him
Without any rein,
The stallion of heaven
The steed of the skies,
The horse of the singer
Who sings as he flies.

ELEANOR FARJEON

AS LUCY WENT A-WALKING

As Lucy went a-walking one morning cold and fine,
There sate three crows upon a bough, and three times
    three are nine:
Then "O!" said Lucy, in the snow, "it's very plain to see
A witch has been a-walking in the fields in front of me."

Then stept she light and heedfully across the frozen
    snow,
And plucked a bunch of elder-twigs that near a pool
    did grow;
And, by and by, she comes to seven shadows in one
    place
Stretched black by seven poplar-trees against the sun's
    bright face.

She looks to left, she looks to right, and in the midst
    she sees
A little pool of water clear and frozen 'neath the trees;

Then down beside its margent in the crusted snow she
   kneels,
And hears a magic belfry, ringing with sweet bells.

Clear rang the faint far merry peal, then silence on the
   air,
And icy-still the frozen pool and poplars standing
   there:
Then, soft, as Lucy turned her head and looked along
   the snow
She sees a witch—a witch she sees, come frisking to
   and fro.

Her scarlet, buckled shoes they clicked, her heels
   a-twinkling high;
With mistletoe her steeple-hat bobbed as she capered
   by;
But never a dint, or mark, or print, in the whiteness
   there to see,
Though danced she light, though danced she fast,
   though danced she lissomely.

It seemed 'twas diamonds in the air, or tiny flakes of
   frost;
It seemed 'twas golden smoke around, or sunbeams
   lightly tossed;
It seemed an elfin music like to reeds' and warblers'
   rose:
"Nay!" Lucy said, "it is the wind that through the
   branches flows."

And as she peeps, and as she peeps, 'tis no more one,
   but three,
And eye of bat, and downy wing of owl within the tree,

_____
51

And the bells of that sweet belfry a-pealing as before,
And now it is not three she sees, and now it is not four.

"O! who are ye," sweet Lucy cries, "that in a dreadful
    ring,
All muffled up in brindled shawls, do caper, frisk, and
    spring?"
"A witch and witches, one and nine," they straight to
    her reply,
And look upon her narrowly, with green and needle
    eye.

Then Lucy sees in clouds of gold sweet cherry trees
    upgrow,
And bushes of red roses that bloomed above the snow;
She smells all faint the almond-boughs blowing so
    wild and fair,
And doves with milky eyes ascend fluttering in the air.

Clear flowers she sees, like tulip buds, go floating by
    like birds,
With wavering tips that warbled sweetly strange
    enchanted words;
And as with ropes of amethyst the twigs with lamps
    were hung,
And clusters of green emeralds like fruit upon them
    clung.

"O witches nine, ye dreadful nine, O witches three
    times three."
Whence come these wondrous things that I this
    Christmas morning see?"
But straight, as in a clap, when she of "Christmas"
    says the word,

———

Here is the snow, and there the sun, but never bloom
   nor bird;

Nor warbling flame, nor gloaming-rope of amethyst
   there shows,
Nor bunches of green emeralds, nor belfry, well, and
   rose,
Nor cloud of gold, nor cherry-tree, nor witch in
   brindled shawl,
But like a dream which vanishes, so vanished were
   they all.

When Lucy sees, and only sees three crows upon a
   bough,
And earthly twigs, and brushes hidden white in driven
   snow,
Then "O!" said Lucy, "three times three are nine—I
   plainly see
Some witch has been a-walking in the fields in front of
   me."

WALTER DE LA MARE

SPELLS

I dance and dance without any feet—
This is the spell of the ripening wheat.

With never a tongue I've a tale to tell—
This is the meadow-grasses' spell.

I give you health without any fee—
This is the spell of the apple-tree.

I rhyme and riddle without any book—
This is the spell of the bubbling brook.

Without any legs I run for ever—
This is the spell of the mighty river.

I fall for ever and not at all—
This is the spell of the waterfall.

Without a voice I roar aloud—
This is the spell of the thunder-cloud.

No button or seam has my white coat—
This is the spell of the leaping goat.

JAMES REEVES

SNAIL, MOON AND ROSE

Over the darkness
Creeps the moon,
Singing a small
Invisible tune.

Who has heard him?
None can tell
But the grey snail
In his grey shell.

He too whispers
As he goes,
Moving on strange
Congested toes,

Till every leaf
Has curled her ear
In the echoing
Atmosphere;

And ebony ant
Minute and shy
Pauses to cock
An urgent eye

At the stars and the night
And the great, mad moon
Singing his queer
Demented tune

Whose language not
A creature knows
But the grey snail
And the wet rose.

JEAN   KENWARD

TALL TALES

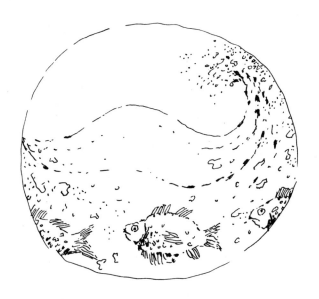

EVE

Eve, with her basket was
Deep in the bells and grass,
Wading in bells and grass
Up to her knees,
Picking a dish of sweet
Berries and plums to eat,
Down in the bells and grass
Under the trees.

Mute as a mouse in a
Corner the cobra lay
Curled round a bough of the
Cinnamon tall. . . .
Now to get even and
Humble proud heaven and
Now was the moment or
Never at all.

"Eva!" Each syllable,
Light as a flower fell,
"Eva!" he whispered the
Wondering maid,
Soft as a bubble sung
Out of a linnet's lung,
Soft and most silvery
"Eva!" he said.

Picture that orchard sprite,
Eve, with her body white,

Supple and smooth to her
Slim finger tips,
Wondering, listening,
Listening, wondering,
Eve with a berry
Half-way to her lips.

Oh had our simple Eve
Seen through the make-believe!
Had she but known the
Pretender he was!
Out of the boughs he came
Whispering still her name,
Tumbling in twenty rings
Into the grass.

Here was the strangest pair
In the world anywhere,
Eve in the bells and grass
Kneeling, and he
Telling his story low . . .
Singing birds saw them go
Down the dark path to
The Blasphemous Tree.

Oh what a clatter when
Titmouse and Jenny Wren
Saw him successful and
Taking his leave!
How they all hated him!
How they all pitied
Poor motherless Eve!

Picture her crying
Outside in the lane,
Eve, with no dish of sweet
Berries and plums to eat,
Haunting the gate of the
Orchard in vain. . . .
Picture the lewd delight
Under the hill tonight—
"Eva!" the toast goes round,
"Eva!" again.

RALPH HODGSON

THE NUT-CRACKERS
AND THE SUGAR-TONGS

The Nut-crackers sate by a plate on the table,
  The Sugar-tongs sate by a plate at his side;
And the Nut-crackers said, "Don't you wish we were
    able
  Along the blue hills and green meadows to ride?
Must we drag on this stupid existence for ever,
  So idle and weary, so full of remorse,—
While every one else takes his pleasure, and never
  Seems happy unless he is riding a horse?

"Don't you think we could ride without being in-
    structed?
  Without any saddle, or bridle, or spur?
Our legs are so long, and so aptly constructed,
  I'm sure that an accident could not occur.
Let us all of a sudden hop down from the table,
  And hustle downstairs, and each jump on a horse!
Shall we try? Shall we go? Do you think we are able?"
  The Sugar-tongs answered distinctly, "Of course!"

So down the long staircase they hopped in a minute,
  The Sugar-tongs snapped, and the Crackers said
    "Crack!"
The stable was open, the horses were in it;
  Each took out a pony, and jumped on its back.
The Cat in a fright scrambled out of the doorway,
  The Mice tumbled out of a bundle of hay,
The brown and the white Rats, and the black ones
    from Norway,
  Screamed out, "They are taking the horses away!"

The whole of the household was filled with amazement,
   The Cups and the Saucers danced wildly about,
The Plates and the Dishes looked out of the casement,
   The Salt-cellar stood on his head with a shout,
The Spoons with a clatter looked out of the lattice,
   The Mustard-pot climbed up the Gooseberry Pies,
The Soup-ladle peeped through a heap of Veal Patties,
   And squeaked with a ladle-like scream of surprise.

The Frying-pan said, "It's an awful delusion!"
   The Tea-kettle hissed and grew black in the face;
And they all rushed downstairs in the wildest con-
     fusion,
   To see the great Nut-cracker-Sugar-tong race.
And out of the stable, with screamings and laughter,
   (Their ponies were cream-coloured, speckled with
     brown),
The Nut-crackers first, and the Sugar-tongs after,
   Rode all round the yard and then all round the town.

They rode through the street, and they rode by the
     station,
   They galloped away to the beautiful shore;
In silence they rode, and made no observation,
   Save this: "We will never go back any more!"
And still you might hear till they rode out of hearing
   The Sugar-tongs snap, and the Crackers say
     "Crack!"
Till far in the distance, their forms disappearing,
   They faded away.—And they never came back!

EDWARD LEAR

LUCK

What brings you, sailor, home from the sea—
Coffers of gold and of ivory?

When first I went to sea as a lad
A new jack-knife was all I had;

And I've sailed for fifty years and three
To the coasts of gold and of ivory:

And now at the end of a lucky life,
Well, still I've got my old jack-knife.

WILFRID GIBSON

CORTEZ

Cortez one night trod
The deck alone;
In the high heaven
A great moon shone,

A golden fruit
Of the vast tree
Whose blue, still branches
Sweep the sea.

With questing gaze
That captain dreamed
As the gold pathway
Shook and gleamed,

But to his gaze
Hungry and tense
Burned not that broad
Magnificence,

Seeing no beauty,
Seeing but bars
Of gold and silver
And gems like stars,

Silks and emeralds,
Ivory and furs,
And strange new plunder
From foreign curs.

Plunged the ship on
Through cresting seas,

With no land risen
To give him ease,

But to his soul
And his soul's sight
Shaped allurements
Of fierce delight:

Treasure looted
With pike and sword,
And cowering slaves
Dumb to his word;

Ships and sailormen,
Fire and death,
And glory, glory
With every breath.

Cortez that night trod
The deck alone:
In his dark soul
A red moon shone.

WILLIAM KEAN SEYMOUR

THE SAILOR AND THE SHARK

There was a queen that fell in love with a jolly sailor
    bold,
But he shipped to the Indies, where he would seek for
    gold.
All in a good sea-boat, my boys, we fear no wind that
    blows!

There was a king that had a fleet of ships both tall and
    tarred;
He carried off this pretty queen, and she jumped over-
    board.
All in a good sea-boat, my boys, we fear no wind that
    blows!

The queen, the queen is overboard! a shark was cruis-
    ing round,
He swallowed up this dainty bit alive and safe and
    sound.
All in a good sea-boat, my boys, we fear no wind that
    blows!

Within the belly of this shark it was both dark and
    cold,
But she was faithful still and true to her jolly sailor
    bold.
All in a good sea-boat, my boys, we fear no wind that
    blows!

The shark was sorry for her, and swam away so fast,
In the Indies, where the camels are, he threw her up
    at last.

*All in a good sea-boat, my boys, we fear no wind that
     blows!*

On one of the same goodly beasts, all in a palanquin,
She spied her own true love again—the Emperor of
     Tonquin!
*All in a good sea-boat, my boys, we fear no wind that
     blows!*

She called to him "O stay, my love, your queen is come,
     my dear."
"Oh I've a thousand queens more fair within my king-
     dom here."
*All in a good sea-boat, my boys, we fear no wind that
     blows!*

"You smell of the grave so strong, my dear." "I've
     sailed in a shark," says she.
"It's not of the grave I smell; but I smell of the fish of
     the sea."
*All in a good sea-boat, my boys, we fear no wind that
     blows!*

"My lady loves they smell so sweet; of rice-paper so
     fine.
The queen the King of Paris loves no sweeter smells
     than mine!"
*All in a good sea-boat, my boys, we fear no wind that
     blows!*

She got aboard the shark again, and weeping went her
     way;
The shark swam back so fast to where the tall ships
     lay.

*All in a good sea-boat, my boys, we fear no wind that
    blows!*

The king he got the queen again, the shark away he
    swam.
The queen was merry as could be, and mild as any
    lamb.
*All in a good sea-boat, my boys, we fear no wind that
    blows!*

Now all you pretty maidens what love a sailor bold,
You'd better ship along with him before his love grows
    cold.

FREDERICK YORK POWELL
(*from the French of Paul Fort*)

THE BALLAD OF THE OYSTERMAN

It was a tall young oysterman lived by the river-side,
His shop was just upon the bank, his boat was on the
    tide;
The daughter of a fisherman, that was so straight and
    slim,
Lived over on the other bank, right opposite to him.

It was the pensive oysterman that saw a lovely maid,
Upon a moonlight evening, a-sitting in the shade!
He saw her wave her handkerchief, as much as if to
    say,
"I'm wide awake, young oysterman, and all the folks
    away."

Then up arose the oysterman, and to himself said he,
"I guess I'll leave the skiff at home, for fear that folks
    should see;
I read it in the story-book, that, for to kiss his dear,
Leander swam the Hellespont—and I will swim this
    here,"

And he has leaped into the waves, and crossed the
    shining stream,
And he has clambered up the bank, all in the moon-
    light gleam;
Oh, there were kisses sweet as dew, and words as soft
    as rain,—
But they have heard her father's step, and in he leaps
    again!

Out spoke the ancient fisherman: "Oh, what was that,
my daughter?"
"'Twas nothing but a pebble, sir, I threw into the
water."
"And what is that, pray tell me, love, that paddles off
so fast?"
"It's nothing but a porpoise, sir, that's been a-swim-
ming past."

Out spoke the ancient fisherman: "Now bring me my
harpoon!
I'll get into my fishing-boat, and fix the fellow soon."
Down fell that pretty innocent, as falls a snow-white
lamb!
Her hair drooped round her pallid cheeks, like seaweed on a clam.

Alas for those two loving ones! she waked not from
her swound,
And he was taken with the cramp, and in the waves
was drowned!
But Fate has metamorphosed them, in pity of their
woe,
And now they keep an oyster-shop for mermaids down
below.

OLIVER WENDELL HOLMES

LEAVE HER, JOHNNY

I thought I heard the captain say:
    Leave her, Johnny, leave her!
You may go ashore and touch your pay,
    It's time for us to leave her.

The winds were foul, the trip was long;
    Leave her, Johnny, leave her;
But before we go we'll sing a song,
    It's time for us to leave her.

The winds were foul, the work was hard—
    Leave her, Johnny, leave her;
From Liverpool docks to Brooklyn Yard;
    It's time for us to leave her.

She'd neither steer, not stay, nor wear;
    Leave her, Johnny, leave her;
She shipped it green and made us swear;
    It's time for us to leave her.

She'd neither wear, nor steer, nor stay:
    Leave her, Johnny, leave her;
Her running rigging carried away:
    It's time for us to leave her.

ANON

A FOX JUMPED UP

A fox jumped up one winter's night,
And begged the moon to give him light,
For he'd many miles to trot that night
Before he reached his den O!
     Den O! Den O!
For he'd many miles to trot that night
Before he reached his den O!

The first place he came to was a farmer's yard,
Where the ducks and the geese declared it hard
That their nerves should be shaken and their rest so
   marred
By a visit from Mr. Fox O!
     Fox O! Fox O!
That their nerves should be shaken and their rest so
   marred
By a visit from Mr. Fox O!

He took the grey goose by the neck
And swung him right across his back;
The grey goose cried out, Quack, quack, quack,
With his legs hanging dangling down O!
     Down O! Down O!
The grey goose cried out, Quack, quack, quack,
With his legs hanging dangling down O!

Old mother Slipper Slopper jumped out of bed,
And out of the window she popped her head:
Oh! John, John, John, the grey goose is gone,
And the fox is off to his den O!
     Den O! Den O!

Oh! John, John, John, the grey goose is gone,
And the fox is off to his den O!

John ran up to the top of the hill,
And blew his whistle loud and shrill;
Said the fox, That is very pretty music, still—
I'd rather be in my den O!
      Den O! Den O!
Said the fox, That is very pretty music, still—
I'd rather be in my den O!

The fox went back to his hungry den,
And his dear little foxes, eight, nine, ten;
Quoth they, Good daddy, you must go there again,
If you bring such good cheer from the farm O!
      Farm O! Farm O!
Quoth they, Good daddy, you must go there again,
If you bring such good cheer from the farm O!

The fox and his wife, without any strife,
Said they never ate a better goose in all their life;
They did very well without fork or knife,
And the little ones picked the bones O!
      Bones O! Bones O!
They did very well without fork or knife
And the little ones picked the bones O!

ANON

AS I WENT OVER THE WATER

As I went over the water.
   The water went over me.
I saw two little blackbirds
   Sitting on a tree;
One called me a rascal,
   And one called me a thief,
I took up my little black stick
   And knocked out all their teeth.

NURSERY RHYME

THE DANIEL JAZZ

*Let the leader train the audience to roar
like lions, to join in the refrain, "Go chain
the lions down," before he begins to lead
them in this jazz.*

Darius the Mede was a king and a wonder.   *Beginning*
His eye was proud, and his voice like   *with a*
   thunder.   *strain of*
He kept bad lions in a monstrous den.   *Dixie.*
He fed up the lions on Christian men.

Daniel was the chief hired man of the   *With a*
   land.   *touch of*
He stirred up the jazz in the palace band. *Alexander's*
He whitewashed the cellar. He shoveled *Ragtime*
   in the coal.   *Band.*
And Daniel kept a-praying: "Lord, save my soul."
Daniel kept a-praying: "Lord, save my soul."
Daniel kept a-praying: "Lord, save my soul."

Daniel was the butler, swagger and swell.
He ran upstairs. He answered the bell.
And *he* would let in whoever came a-calling:
Saints so holy, scamps so appalling.
"Old man Ahab leaves his card.
Elisha and the bears are a-waiting in the yard.

Here comes Pharaoh and his snakes a-calling.
Here comes Cain and his wife a-calling.
Shadrach, Meshach and Abednego for tea.
Here comes Jonah and the whale,
And the *Sea!*

Here comes St. Peter and his fishing pole.
Here comes Judas and his silver a-calling.
Here comes old Beelzebub a-calling."
And Daniel kept a-praying: "Lord, save my soul."
Daniel kept a-praying: "Lord, save my soul."
Daniel kept a-praying: "Lord, save my soul."

His sweetheart and his mother were Christian and
    meek.
They washed and ironed for Darius every week.
One Thursday he met them at the door:
Paid them as usual, but acted sore.
He said: "Your Daniel is a dead little pigeon.
He's a good hard worker, but he talks religion."
And he showed them Daniel in the lions' cage.
Daniel standing quietly, the lions in a rage.

His good old mother cried:—
"Lord, save him."
And Daniel's tender sweetheart cried:
"Lord, save him."

And she was a golden lily in the dew.
And she was as sweet as an apple on the tree,
And she was as fine as a melon in the corn-field,
Gliding and lovely as a ship on the sea,
Gliding and lovely as a ship on the sea.

And she prayed to the Lord:—
"*Send* Gabriel. *Send* Gabriel."
King Darius said to the lions:—
"Bite Daniel. Bite Daniel.
Bite him. Bite him. Bite him!"

———

Thus roared the lions:—
"We want Daniel, Daniel, Daniel,
We want Daniel, Daniel, Daniel.
Grrrrrrrrrrrrrrrrrrrrrrrrrrrrrrrr
Grrrrrrrrrrrrrrrrrrrrrrrrrrrrrrrrrr"
And Daniel did not frown,
Daniel did not cry.
He kept on looking at the sky.
And the Lord said to Gabriel:—
"Go chain the lions down,
Go chain the lions down,
Go chain the lions down.
Go chain the lions down."
And *Gabriel* chained the lions,
And *Gabriel* chained the lions,
And *Gabriel* chained the lions,
And Daniel got out of the den,
And Daniel got out of the den,
And Daniel got out of the den.
And Darius said: "You're a Christian child,"
Darius said: "You're a Christian child,"
Darius said: "You're a Christian child,"
And gave him his job again,
And gave him his job again,
And gave him his job again.

Here the audience roars with the leader.

The audience sings this with the leader, to the old Negro tune.

VACHEL LINDSAY

MY HAT

Mother said if I wore this hat
I should be certain to get off with the right sort of chap
We look where I am now, on a desert island
With so far as I can see no one at all on hand
I know what has happened though I suppose Mother
    wouldn't see
This hat being so strong has completely run away with
    me
I had the feeling it was beginning to happen the
    moment I put it on
What a moment that was as I rose up, I rose up like a
    flying swan
As strong as a swan too, why see how far my hat has
    flown me away
It took us a night to come and then a night and a day
And all the time the swan wing in my hat waved
    beautifully
Ah, I thought, How this hat becomes me.
First the sea was dark but then it was pale blue
And still the wing beat and we flew and we flew
A night and a day and a night, and by the old right way
Between the sun and the moon we flew until morning
    day.
It is always early mornings here on this peculiar island
The green grass grows into the sea on the dipping land
Am I glad to be here? Yes, well, I am,
It's nice to be rid of Father, Mother and the young man
There's just one thing causes me a twinge of pain,
If I take my hat off, shall I find myself home again?
So in this early morning land I always wear my hat
Go home, you see, I wouldn't run a risk like that.

STEVIE SMITH

THE WEED

Don't pull me up! I got to live,
The same as what you got to do,
And uman people never give
A thought to what a weed goes through—
Unted and acked and oed to death
We ardly dror a peaceful breath.

I dessay now you love your Mum,
And mind the things she as to say:
Don't think of me as thievin scum—
I'm a good daughter in my way;
There ain't a plant, there ain't a grass
A better weed than Mother was.

Er figger was a sight to see!
So round and full in the rosette;
And then er way—so bright and free,
Taking what umus she could get,
And when our earts was in our boots,
Saying, "Cheer up! you got your roots!"

She ad er roots all right, ad Ma,
As Tom the gardener's boy could tell;
E said they reached Australia
And sometimes that they went to—well,
E'd lug the tops off poor old Mum,
But in a fortnight up she'd come.

She knew the ropes, did Mum, all right,
"Grow near some borjwar plant," she'd say
"What's like yourself, and ide from sight
Till everyone's on oliday.

Then bloom at such a crackin pace
That weeds will fill the blinkin place!"

And ow my Mum did 'ate the plants
You silly people love to grow,
And ow she did egg on the ants
To muck their roots up from below,
The wireworms and the capsid bugs—
And ow she lectured them old slugs!

"You boys can get about," says she;
"Good Lor! if I could do the same,
I wouldn't leave a single tree,
Or any veg, what's worth the name;
I'm sick of all the lot of you,
The bits of damage what you do!

Go on! ave them carnations down!
Climb up them roses, and them beans!
Spit on them lilies, turn 'em brown,
And show what reverlootion means!
One good night's work ud wreck the show!
Ooray, me brave lads! orf you go!"

Them slugs they never stopped to think!
They all came out from underground,
And lumme! they ad all turned pink,
And made a norrid flappin sound
Like dishrags blowin overead,
They run so fast at what she said!

And all the night we eared em munch,
And all night long we eared em chew;
At first the ole outrageous bunch,
And then we only eared a few;

At last, O orrors! we eared pops,
And then a lot of flabby flops.

At lenth there came the gashly dawn—
And we could see, on every side,
Their pore white bodies on the lawn;
And on the paths split open wide
Was them dead eroes that ad bust
To wreck the garden Mum ad cussed!

Pore Mum she shivered, and the dew
Fell off er flowers like angel's tears;
She says, "I bin the death of you,
That was such good ardworkin dears;
And there you lay like bits of dough!
Not bloomin well for nothing, though!"

And then she drored erself up straight—
I never see er look so fine—
And bellered, "Thus we demonstrate
The will of weeds as is divine!
Ow richly they ave earned their rests
To win the world for weeds and pests!"

But Mum she never moped for long;
She shook erself and stretched er shoots,
And swelled er buds out big and strong,
And felt about with all her roots,
Tryin er best to make quite sure
No garden plant should get manure.

Oh, it was lovely when a bee
Come to Mum's flowers and made er giggle;
Of course it was all Greek to me,

But I just loved to see er wriggle:
And once I said, "Mum, are bees nice?"
I ad no chance to say it twice!

She turned on me like anything!
"You nasty dirty little cat!
You must a bin philanderin
With bees, to say a thing like that!
Such words from me own flesh and blood
Before you've even got a bud!"

Of course I understand it now,
For Mum, she told me later on,
That bees what come when flowers blow
Are like a weddin to each one,
And ow she thought a peony
Ad bin the pa of Sis and me.

And we must old our eads up igh,
Because we was not common weeds,
And grow like anything, and try
To make the most of all our seeds;
But 'ate the posh flowers just the same,
Because they'd grudged us poor pa's name.

I ope I shall repay er trust,
And not forget er lovely words,
Nor them eroic slugs what bust
And left their bodies to the birds;
It elps in all our goins on
To think of loved ones as is gone.

For our dear Ma she is no more!
I never shall forget the day

When Mr. Thompson raged and swore,
And said e'd turn young Tom away
For leavin weeds as big as Mum
And lettin lots of others come.

The boy e muttered something rude,
And moaned a bit about his wrongs,
And ow e was misunderstood—
Then fetched a fork with orrid prongs,
A basket, and a nasty spud,
And said e'd ave our mother's blood!

Jab went the fork—it turned me bad,
E stuck it in so far below
Poor Mum—a gruntin from the lad
I eard—I eard er taproot go!
Er roots laid naked in the sun:
E'd got the lot—poor Ma was done.

E flung er on is orrid eap,
To wither all the long day through,
But all the time poor Mum would keep
Calling to us; although she knew
She was a goner, yet she tried
To keep our earts up till she died.

All the ot day she called and said;
"E missed you young uns, glory be!
You'll be alive when I am dead,
So don't you go and grieve for me!
Take all the umus you can get!
Suckers and seeds! We'll beat em yet!"

Suckers and seeds! the weeds will win!
We'll get the ole world for our own!

Then Oh ow glorious will come in
The era of the great Self-sown!
Ave you the eart to kill me now,
After my touchin story? . . . OW!!!

RUTH PITTER

THE FORSAKEN MERMAN

Come, dear children, let us away;
Down and away below!
Now my brothers call from the bay,
Now the great winds shoreward blow,
Now the salt tides seaward flow;
Now the wild white horses play,
Champ and chafe and toss in the spray,
Children, dear, let us away!
This way! This way!

Call her once before you go—
Call once yet!
In a voice that she will know:
"Margaret! Margaret!"
Children's voices, should be dear
(Call once more) to a mother's ear;
Children's voices, wild with pain—
Surely she will come again!
Call her once and come away;
This way, this way!
"Mother dear, we cannot stay!

The wild white horses foam and fret."
Margaret! Margaret!

Come, dear children, come away down;
Call no more!
One last look at the white-walled town,
And the little grey church on the windy shore
Then come down!
She will not come though you call all day;
Come away, come away!

Children dear, was it yesterday
We heard the sweet bells over the bay?
In the caverns where we lay,
Through the surf and through the swell,
The far off sound of a silver bell?
Sand-strewn caverns, cool and deep,
Where the winds are all asleep;
Where the spent lights quiver and gleam,
Where the salt weed sways in the stream,
Where the sea-beasts ranged all round,
Feed in the ooze of their pasture-ground;
Where the sea-snakes coil and twine,
Dry their mail and bask in the brine;
Where great whales come sailing by,
Sail and sail, with unshut eye,
Round the world for ever and aye?
When did music come this way?
Children dear, was it yesterday?

Children dear, was it yesterday
(Call yet once) that she went away?
Once she sat with you and me,

On a red gold throne in the heart of the sea,
And the youngest sat on her knee.
She combed its bright hair, and she tended it well,
When down swung the sound of a far-off bell.
She sighed, she looked up through the clear green sea;
She said: "I must go, for my kinsfolk pray
In the little grey church on the shore today.
'Twill be Easter-time in the world—ah me!
And I lose my poor soul, Merman, here with thee."
I said: "Go up, dear heart, through the waves;
Say thy prayer, and come back to the kind sea-caves!"
She smiled, she went up through the surf in the bay.
Children dear, was it yesterday?

Children dear, were we long alone?
"The sea grows stormy, the little ones moan;
Long prayers," I said, "in the world they say;
Come!" I said; and we rose through the surf in the bay.
We went up the beach, by the sandy down
Where the sea-stocks bloom, to the white-walled town;
Through the narrow paved streets, where all was still,
To the little grey church on the windy hill.
From the church came a murmur of folk at their
    prayers,
But we stood without in the cold blowing airs.
We climbed on the graves, on the stones worn with
    rains,
And we gazed up the aisle through the small leaded
    panes.
She sat by the pillar; we saw her clear;
"Margaret, hist! come quick, we are here!
Dear heart," I said, "We are long alone;
The sea grows stormy, the little ones moan."
But, ah, she never gave me a look,

———
86

For her eyes were sealed to the holy book!
Loud prays the priest; shut stands the door.
Come away, children, call no more!
Come away, come down, call no more!

Down, down, down!
Down to the depths of the sea!
She sits at her wheel in the humming town,
Singing most joyfully,
Hark what she sings: "O joy, O joy,
For the humming street and the child with its toy!
For the priest, and the bell, and the holy well;
For the wheel where I spun,
And the blessed light of the sun!"
And so she sings her fill,
Singing most joyfully,
Till the spindle drops from her hand,
And the whizzing wheel stands still.
She steals to the window, and looks at the sand,
And over the sand at the sea;
And her eyes are set in a stare;
And anon there breaks a sigh
And anon there drops a tear,
From a sorrow-clouded eye,
And a heart sorrow-laden,
A long, long sigh;
For the cold strange eyes of a little mermaiden
And the gleam of her golden hair.

Come away, away children;
Come children, come down!
The hoarse wind blows coldly;
Lights shine in the town
She will start from her slumber

When gusts shake the door;
She will hear the winds howling,
Will hear the waves roar.
We shall see, while above us
The waves roar and whirl,
A ceiling of amber,
A pavement of pearl.
Singing: "Here comes a mortal,
But faithless was she!
And alone dwell for ever
The kings of the sea!"

But, children, at midnight,
When soft the winds blow,
When clear falls the moonlight,
When spring-tides are low;
When sweet airs come seaward
From heaths starred with broom,
And high rocks thrown mildly
On the blanched sands a gloom;
Up the still, glistening beaches,
Up the creeks we will hie,
Over banks of bright seaweed
The ebb-tide leaves dry.
We will gaze, from the sand-hills,
At the white, sleeping town;
At the church on the hill-side—
And then come back down.
Singing: "There dwells a loved one,
But cruel is she!
She left lonely for ever
The kings of the sea."

MATTHEW ARNOLD

FIRST FIGHT

Tonight, then, is the night;
Stretched on the massage table,
Wrapped in his robe, he breathes
Liniment and sweat
And tries to close his ears
To the roaring of the crowd,
A murky sea of noise
That bears upon its tide
The frail sound of the bell
And brings the cunning fear
That he might not do well,
Not fear of bodily pain
But that his tight-lipped pride
Might be sent crashing down,
His white ambition slain,
Knocked spinning the glittering crown.
How could his spirit bear
That ignominious fall?
Not hero but a clown
Spurned or scorned by all.
The thought appals, and he
Feels sudden envy for
The roaring crowd outside
And wishes he were there
Anonymous and safe,
Calm in the tolerant air,
Would almost choose to be
Anywhere but here.

II

The door blares open suddenly,
The room is sluiced with row;
His second says "We're on next fight,
We'd better get going now.
You got your gumshield, haven't you?
Just loosen up—that's right—
Don't worry, Boy, you'll be O.K.
Once you start to fight."

Out of the dressing-room, along
The neutral passage to
The yelling cavern where the ring
Through the haze of blue
Tobacco smoke is whitewashed by
The aching glare of light:
Geometric ropes are stretched as taut
As this boy's nerves are tight.

And now he's in his corner where
He tries to look at ease;
He feels the crowd's sharp eyes as they
Prick and pry and tease;
He hears them murmur like the sea
Or some great dynamo:
They are not hostile yet they wish
To see his lifeblood flow.
His adversary enters now;
The boy risks one quick glance;
He does not see any enemy
But something there by chance,
Not human even, but a cold

Abstraction to defeat,
A problem to be solved by guile,
Quick hands, and knowing feet.
The fighters' names are shouted out;
They leave their corners for
The touch of gloves and brief commands;
The disciplines of war.
Back in their corners, stripped of robes,
They hear the bell clang ONE
Brazen syllable which says
The battle has begun.

III

Bite on gumshield
Guard held high,
The crowd are silenced
All sounds die.
Lead with the left,
Again, again;
Watch for the opening,
Feint and then
Hook to the body
But he's blocked it and
Slammed you back
With a fierce right hand.
Hang on grimly
The fog will clear,
Sweat in you nostrils
Grease and fear.
You're hurt and staggering,

Shocked to know
That the story's altered:
He's the hero!

But the mist is clearing,
The referee snaps
A rapid warning
And he smartly taps
Your hugging elbow
And then you step back
Ready to counter
The next attack,
But the first round finishes
Without mishap.
You suck in the air
From the towel's skilled flap.
A voice speaks urgently
Close to your ear:
"Keep your left going, Boy,
Stop him getting near."
He wants to get close to you,
So jab him off hard;
When he tries to slip below,
Never mind your guard,
Crack him with a solid right
Hit him on the chin,
A couple downstairs
And then he'll pack it in!

Slip in the gumshield
Bite on it hard,
Keep him off with your left,
Never drop your guard.

Try a left hook,
But he crosses with a right
Smack on your jaw
And Guy Fawkes night
Flashes and dazzles
Inside you skull,
Your knees go bandy
And you almost fall.
Keep the left jabbing,
Move around the ring,
Don't let him catch you with
Another hook or swing.
Keep your left working,
Keep it up high,
Stab it out straight and hard,
Again—above the eye.
Sweat in the nostrils,
But nothing now of fear,
You're moving smooth and confident
In comfortable gear.
Jab with the left again,
Quickly move away;
Feint and stab another in,
See him duck and sway.
NOW for the pay-off punch,
Smash it hard inside;
It thuds against his jaw, he falls,
Limbs spread wide.
And suddenly you hear the roar
Hoarse music of the crowd,
Voicing your hot ecstasy
Triumphant, male and proud.

IV

Now, in the sleepless darkness of his room
The Boy, in bed, remembers. Suddenly
The victory tastes sour. The man he fought
Was not a thing, as lifeless as a broom
He was a man who hoped and trembled too;
What of him now? What was *he* going through?
And then the Boy bites hard on resolution:
Fighters can't pack pity with their gear,
And yet a bitter taste stays with the notion;
He's forced to swallow down one treacherous tear.
But that's the last. He is a boy no longer;
He is a man, a fighter, such as jeer
At those who make salt beads with melting eyes,
Whatever might cry out, is hurt, or dies.

VERNON SCANNELL

ODD BODS

THERE WAS A LITTLE WOMAN

There was a little woman,
    As I have heard tell,
She went to markct
    Her eggs for to sell;
She went to market
    All on a market day,
And she fell asleep
    On the King's highway.

There came by a pedlar,
    His name was Stout,
He cut her petticoats
    All round about;
He cut her petticoats
    Up to her knees;
Which made the little woman
    To shiver and sneeze.

When this little woman
    Began to awake,
She began to shiver,
    And she began to shake,
She began to shake,
    And she began to cry,
Lawk a mercy on me,
    This is none of I!

But if this be I,
    As I do hope it be,
I have a little dog at home
    And he knows me;

If it be I,
    He'll wag his little tail,
And if it be not I
    He'll loudly bark and wail!

Home went the little woman
    All in the dark,
Up starts the little dog,
    And he began to bark;
He began to bark
    And she began to cry,
Lawk a mercy on me,
    This is none of I!

NURSERY RHYME

ROMAN WALL BLUES

Over the heather the wet wind blows,
I've lice in my tunic and a cold in my nose.

The rain comes pattering out of the sky,
I'm a Wall soldier, I don't know why.

The mist creeps over the hard grey stone.
My girl's in Tungria; I sleep alone.

Aulus goes hanging around her place,
I don't like his manners, I don't like his face.

Piso's a Christian, he worships a fish;
There'd be no kissing if he had his wish.

She gave me a ring but I diced it away;
I want my girl and I want my pay.

When I'm a veteran with only one eye
I shall do nothing but look at the sky.

W. H. AUDEN

TO A FAT LADY
SEEN FROM THE TRAIN

O why do you walk through the fields in gloves,
    Missing so much and so much?
O fat white woman whom nobody loves,
Why do you walk through the fields in gloves,
When the grass is soft as the breast of doves
    And shivering-sweet to the touch?
O why do you walk through the fields in gloves,
    Missing so much and so much.

FRANCES CORNFORD

THE AKOND OF SWAT

Who, or why, or which, or *what*, is the Akond of
  SWAT?

Is he tall or short, or dark or fair?
Does he sit on a stool or a sofa or chair, or SQUAT,
                        The Akond of Swat?

Is he wise, or foolish, young or old?
Does he drink his soup and his coffee cold, or HOT,
                        The Akond of Swat?

Does he sing or whistle, jabber or talk
And when riding abroad does he gallop or walk, or
  TROT,
                        The Akond of Swat?

Does he wear a turban, a fez, or a hat?
Does he sleep on a mattress, a bed, or a mat, or a COT,
                        The Akond of Swat?

When he writes a copy in round-hand size,
Does he cross his T's and finish his I's with a DOT,
                        The Akond of Swat?

Can he write a letter concisely clear
Without a speck or a smudge or smear, or BLOT,
                        The Akond of Swat?

Do his people like him extremely well?
Or do they, whenever they can, rebel, or PLOT,
                        At the Akond of Swat?

If he catches them then, either old or young,
Does he have them chopped in pieces or hung, or *shot*,
$\qquad\qquad$ The Akond of Swat?

Do his people prig in the lanes or park?
Or even at times when days are dark, GAROTTE?
$\qquad\qquad$ O the Akond of Swat!

Does he study the wants of his own dominion?
Or doesn't he care for public opinion a JOT,
$\qquad\qquad$ The Akond of Swat?

To amuse his mind do his people show him
Pictures, or anyone's last new poem, or WHAT,
$\qquad\qquad$ For the Akond of Swat?

At night if he suddenly screams and wakes,
Do they bring him only a few small cakes, or a LOT,
$\qquad\qquad$ For the Akond of Swat?

Does he live on turnips, tea, or tripe?
Does he like his shawl to be marked with a stripe or a
$\quad$ SPOT,
$\qquad\qquad$ The Akond of Swat?

Does he like to lie on his back in a boat
Like the lady who lived in that isle remote,
$\quad$ SHALLOTT,
$\qquad\qquad$ The Akond of Swat?

Is he quiet, or always making a fuss?
Is his steward a Swiss or a Swede or a Russ, or a
$\quad$ SCOT,
$\qquad\qquad$ The Akond of Swat?

Does he like to sit by the calm blue wave?
Or to sleep and snore in a dark green cave, or a
   GROTT,
                              The Akond of Swat?

Does he drink small beer from a silver jug?
Or a bowl? or a glass? or a cup? or a mug? or a POT,
                              The Akond of Swat?

Does he beat his wife with a gold-topped pipe,
When she lets the gooseberries grow too ripe, or ROT,
                              The Akond of Swat?

Does he wear a white tie when he dines with friends,
And tie it neat in a bow with ends, or a KNOT,
                              The Akond of Swat?

Does he like new cream, and hate mince-pies?
When he looks at the sun does he wink his eyes, or
   NOT,
                              The Akond of Swat?

Does he teach his subjects to roast and bake?
Does he sail about on an inland lake, in a YACHT,
                              The Akond of Swat?

Someone, or nobody, knows I wot
Who or which or why or what
                              Is the Akond of Swat!

                              EDWARD LEAR

A DRESSMAKER

Mrs. Binns
Mrs. Binns
Fills her mouth with
Safety pins;

Now and then she
Takes one out,
Turns and twiddles
Me about,

Talking, as she
Pricks my hip,
Through the corner
Of her lip.

While she lengthens,
Cuts, and measures,
Still her tongue
Confines her treasures. . . .

How I long
To move and see
If she'd swallow
Two or three!

But Mrs. Binns
Is very clever
For she never
Never never

Loses any
Of her pins.
I wish *I* were
Mrs. Binns!

JEAN KENWARD

OLD DAN'L

Out of his cottage to the sun
Bent double comes old Dan'l,
His chest all over cotton wool,
His back all over flannel!

"Winter will finish him" they've said
Each winter now for ten;
But comes the first warm day of Spring
Old Dan'l's out again!

L. A. G. STRONG

THERE WAS A LADY
ALL SKIN AND BONE

There was a lady all skin and bone,
Sure such a lady was never known:
It happened upon a certain day,
This lady went to church to pray.

When she came to the church stile,
There she did rest a little while;
When she came to the churchyard,
There the bells so loud she heard.

When she came to the church door,
She stopped to rest a little more;
When she came the church within,
The parson prayed 'gainst pride and sin.

On looking up, on looking down,
She saw a dead man on the ground;
And from his nose unto his chin,
The worms crawled out, the worms crawled in.

Then she unto the parson said,
Shall I be so when I am dead?
O yes! O yes, the parson said,
You will be so when you are dead.

NURSERY RHYME

MARY'S GHOST

'Twas in the middle of the night,
   To sleep young William tried;
When Mary's ghost came stealing in,
   And stood at his bed-side.

O William dear! O William dear!
   My rest eternal ceases;
Alas! my everlasting peace
   Is broken into pieces.

I thought the last of all my cares
   Would end with my last minute;
But tho' I went to my long home,
   I didn't stay long in it.

The body-snatchers they have come,
   And made a snatch at me;
It's very hard them kind of men
   Won't let a body be!

You thought that I was buried deep,
   Quite decent like and chary,
But from her grave in Mary-bone,
   They've come and boned your Mary.

The arm that used to take your arm
   Is took to Dr. Vyse;
And both my legs are gone to walk
   The hospital at Guy's.

I vowed that you should have my hand,
   But fate gives us denial;

You'll find it there, at Dr. Bell's,
    In spirits and a phial.

As for my feet, the little feet
    You used to call so pretty,
There's one, I know, in Bedford Row,
    The t'other's in the City.

I can't tell where my head is gone,
    But Doctor Carpue can;
As for my trunk, it's all packed up
    To go by Pickford's van.

I wish you'd go to Mr. P.
    And save me such a ride;
I don't half like the outside place,
    They've took for my inside.

The cock it crows—I must be gone!
    My William, we must part!
But I'll be yours in death, altho'
    Sir Astley has my heart.

Don't go to weep upon my grave,
    And think that there I be;
They haven't left an atom there
    Of my anatomie.

THOMAS HOOD

A PIG TALE

Poor Jane Higgins,
She had five piggins
And one got drowned in the Irish Sea.
Poor Jane Higgins,
She had four piggins,
And one flew over a sycamore tree.
Poor Jane Higgins,
She had three piggins,
And one was taken away for pork.
Poor Jane Higgins,
She had two piggins,
And one was sent to the Bishop of Cork.
Poor Jane Higgins,
She had one piggin,
And that was struck by a shower of hail,
So poor Jane Higgins
She had no piggins,
And that's the end of my little pig tale.

JAMES REEVES

ALBERT

Albert loved dogs mostly, though this was absurd
for they always slouched away when he touched their
    fur,
but once, perching on his shoulder, alighted a bird;

a bird alive as fire and magical as that day
when clear-eyed Heloise met Peter Abelard.
Though cats followed him, the bird never flew away.

And dogs pursued the cats which hunted the bird.
Albert loved dogs deeply but was jealously hurt
that they pursued him merely because of the bird;

the bird alive as fire and magical as that day.
So one morning he rises and murders the bird
But then the cats vanished and the dogs went away.

Albert hated dogs after, though this was absurd.

DANNIE ABSE

MEG MERRILIES

Old Meg she was a Gipsy,
   And lived upon the Moors:
Her bed it was the brown heath turf,
   And her house was out of doors.

Her apples were swart blackberries,
   Her currants pods o'broom;
Her wine was dew of the wild white rose,
   Her book a churchyard tomb.

Her Brothers were the craggy hills,
   Her Sisters larchen trees—
Alone with her great family
   She lived as she did please.

No breakfast had she many a morn,
   No dinner many a noon,
And 'stead of supper she would stare
   Full hard against the Moon.

But every morn of woodbine fresh
   She made her garlanding,
And every night the dark glen Yew
   She wove and she would sing.

And with her fingers old and brown
   She plaited Mats o' Rushes,
And gave them to the Cottagers
   She met among the bushes.

Old Meg was brave as Margaret Queen
　　And tall as Amazon:
An old red blanket cloak she wore;
　　A chip hat had she on.
God rest her aged bones somewhere—
　　She died full long agone!

JOHN KEATS

A TRUE STORY

My eldest uncle had an extraordinary habit
Of turning young girls into birds;
He kept them in exquisitely jewelled cages.
How he did it I could not tell,
But only that they were inexplicably beautiful.

He was an elegant gentleman of fifty-six
And lived in a Georgian terrace house in Town
Surrounded by his captives' sumptuous, delicate
　　plumage.
They were rarer than nightingales he used to say
And indeed I suppose they undoubtedly were in their
　　way.

Mostly these girls were "orphans" or "actresses"
And so they were seldom missed.

They longed in their dreams to be beautiful and
     admired,
Or so my uncle said with his faint Edwardian smile,
Though I thought I detected a certain trace of guile.

Of course no one knew but me of his strange passion,
Till one day a careless old fool of a cleaner left
Unlatched to the air the door of a gold prison
And out through an open window a mauve bird flew
Like an angel descending to earth for a god's-eye view.

Alas my uncle never recovered his poise.
He roamed the unholy streets six months without
     pause.
His family were shocked and I alone understood
And wept, when after a night of fantastic alarms
He was found in a park, a naked dead girl in his arms.

JOHN SMITH

ON A TIRED HOUSEWIFE

Here lies a poor woman who was always tired,
She lived in a house where help wasn't hired:
Her last words on earth were: "Dear friends, I am
    going
To where there's no cooking, or washing, or sewing,
For everything there is exact to my wishes,
For where they don't eat there's no washing of dishes.
I'll be where loud anthems will always be ringing,
But having no voice I'll be quit of the singing.
Don't mourn for me now, don't mourn for me never,
I am going to do nothing for ever and ever."

                                 ANON

A YOUNG LADY OF SPAIN

There was a young lady of Spain
Who was dreadfully sick on a train,
    Not once, but again
    And again and again,
And again and again and again.

                                   ANON

THERE WAS A CROOKED MAN

There was a crooked man
And he walked a crooked mile:
He found a crooked sixpence
Beside a crooked stile:
He bought a crooked cat
And it caught a crooked mouse
And they both lived together
In a wee crooked house.

NURSERY RHYME

THE PESSIMIST

Nothing to do but work,
   Nothing to eat but food,
Nothing to wear but clothes,
   To keep one from going nude.

Nothing to breathe but air,
   Quick as a flash 'tis gone;
Nowhere to fall but off,
   Nowhere to stand but on.

Nothing to comb but hair,
   Nowhere to sleep but in bed,
Nothing to weep but tears,
   Nothing to bury but dead.

Nothing to sing but songs,
   Ah, well, alas! alack!
Nowhere to go but out,
   Nowhere to come but back.

Nothing to see but sights,
   Nothing to quench but thirst,
Nothing to have but what we've got.
   Thus through life we are cursed.

Nothing to strike but a gait;
   Everything moves that goes.
Nothing at all but common sense
   Can ever withstand these woes.

B. J. KING

115

MR. KARTOFFEL

Mr. Kartoffel's a whimsical man;
He drinks his beer from a watering-can,
And for no good reason that I can see
He fills his pockets with china tea.
He parts his hair with a knife and fork
And takes his ducks for a Sunday walk.
Says he, "if my wife and I should choose
To wear our stockings outside our shoes,
Plant tulip-bulbs in the baby's pram
And eat tobacco instead of jam,
And fill the bath with cauliflowers,
That's nobody's business at all but ours."
Says Mrs. K., "I may choose to travel
With a sack of grass or a sack of gravel,
Or paint my toes, one black one white,
Or sit on a bird's nest half the night—
But whatever I do that is rum or rare,
I rather think that it's my affair.
So fill up your pockets with stamps and string,
And let us be ready for anything!"
Says Mr. K. to his whimsical wife,
"How can we face the storms of life,
Unless we are ready for anything?"

JAMES REEVES

JAMES HONEYMAN

James Honeyman was a silent child
He didn't laugh or cry;
He looked at his mother
With curiosity.

Mother came up to the nursery,
Peeped through the open door,
Saw him striking matches
Sitting on the nursery floor.

He went to the children's party,
The buns were full of cream;
Sat dissolving sugar
In his tea-cup in a dream.

On his eighth birthday
Didn't care that the day was wet
For by his bedside
Lay a ten-shilling chemistry set.

Teacher said: "James Honeyman's
The cleverest boy we've had,
But he doesn't play with the others
And that, I think, is sad."

While the other boys played football
He worked in the laboratory
Got a scholarship to college,
And a first-class degree.

Kept awake with black coffee,
Took to wearing glasses,

Writing a thesis
On the toxic gases.

Went out into the country,
Went by Green Line bus,
Walked on the Chilterns,
Thought about Phosphorus.

Said: "Lewisite in its day
Was pretty decent stuff,
But under modern conditions
It's not nearly strong enough."

His Tutor sipped his port,
Said: "I think it's clear
That young James Honeyman's
The most brilliant man of his year."

He got a job in research
With Imperial Alkali
Said to himself while shaving:
"I'll be famous before I die."

His landlady said: "Mr. Honeyman,
You've only got one life,
You ought to have some fun, Sir.
You ought to find a wife."

At Imperial Alkali
There was a girl called Doreen,
One day she cut her finger,
Asked him for iodine.

"I'm feeling faint," she said.
He led her to a chair,

Fetched her a glass of water,
Wanted to stroke her hair.

They took a villa on the Great West Road,
Painted green and white;
On their left a United Dairy,
A cinema on the right.

At the bottom of his garden
He built a little shed.
"He's going to blow us up,"
All the neighbours said.

Doreen called down at midnight
"Jim dear, it's time for bed."
"I'll finish my experiment
And then I'll come," he said.

Caught influenza at Christmas,
The Doctor said: "Go to bed,"
"I'll finish my experiment
And then I'll go," he said.

Walked out on Sundays,
Helped to push the pram,
Said: "I'm looking for a gas, dear;
A whiff will kill a man.

"I'm going to find it,
That's what I'm going to do."
Doreen squeezed his hand and said:
"Jim, I believe in you."

In the hot nights of summer
When the roses were all red

James Honeyman was working
In his little garden shed.

Came upstairs at midnight,
Kissed his sleeping son,
Held up a sealed glass test-tube,
Said: "Look Doreen, I've won!"

They stood together by the window,
The moon was bright and clear.
He said: "At last I've done something
That's worthy of you, dear."

Took a train next morning,
Went up to Whitehall
With the phial in his pocket
To show it to them all.

Sent in his card,
The officials only swore:
"Tell him we're very busy
And show him the door."

Doreen said to the neighbours:
"Isn't it a shame?
My husband's so clever
And they didn't know his name."

One neighbour was sympathetic,
Her name was Mrs. Flower.
She was the agent
Of a foreign power.

One evening they sat at supper,
There came a gentle knock:

"A gentleman to see Mr. Honeyman."
He stayed till eleven o'clock.

They walked down the garden together,
Down to the little shed;
"We'll see you, then, in Paris.
Good night," the gentleman said.

The boat was nearing Dover
He looked back at Calais:
Said "Honeyman's N.P.C.
Will be heard of, some day."

He was sitting in the garden
Writing notes on a pad,
Their little son was playing
Round his mother and dad.

Suddenly from the east
Some aeroplanes appeared,
Somebody screamed: "They're bombers!
War must have been declared!"

The first bomb hit the Dairy,
The second the cinema,
The third fell in the garden
Just like a falling star.

"Oh kiss me, Mother, kiss me,
And tuck me up in bed
For Daddy's invention
Is going to choke me dead!"

"Where are you, James, where are you?
Oh put your arms around me,

For my lungs are full
Of Honeyman's N.P.C.!"

"I wish I were a salmon
Swimming in the sea,
I wish I were the dove
That coos upon the tree."

"Oh you are not a salmon,
Oh you are not a dove;
But you invented the vapour
That is killing those you love."

"Oh hide me in the mountains,
Oh drown me in the sea.
Lock me in the dungeon
And throw away the key."

"Oh you can't hide in the mountains,
Oh you can't drown in the sea,
But you must die, and you know why,
By Honeyman's N.P.C."

W. H. AUDEN

TIMOTHY WINTERS

Timothy Winters comes to school
With eyes as wide as a football-pool,
Ears like bombs and teeth like splinters:
A blitz of a boy is Timothy Winters.

His belly is white, his neck is dark,
And his hair is an exclamation-mark.
His clothes are enough to scare a crow
And through his britches the blue winds blow.

When teacher talks he won't hear a word
And he shoots down dead the arithmetic-bird,
He licks the patterns off his plate
And he's not even heard of the Welfare State.

Timothy Winters has bloody feet
And he lives in a house on Suez Street,
He sleeps in a sack on the kitchen floor
And they say there aren't boys like him any more.

Old Man Winters likes his beer
And his missus ran off with a bombardier,
Grandma sits in the grate with a gin
And Timothy's dosed with an aspirin.

The Welfare Worker lies awake
But the law's as tricky as a ten-foot snake,
So Timothy Winters drinks his cup
And slowly goes on growing up.

At Morning Prayers the Master helves
For children less fortunate than ourselves,

And the loudest response in the room is when
Timothy Winters roars "Amen!"

So come one angel, come on ten:
Timothy Winters says "Amen,
Amen, amen, amen, amen."
Timothy Winters, Lord.
                          Amen.

                    CHARLES CAUSLEY

TO A FISH

You strange, astonished-looking, angle-faced,
   Dreary-mouthed, gaping wretches of the sea,
   Gulping salt water everlastingly,
Cold-blooded, though with red your blood be graced,
And mute, though dwellers in the roaring waste;
   And you, all shaped beside, that fishy be,—
   Some round, some flat, some long, all devilry,
Legless, unloving, infamously chaste:—

O scaly, slippery, wet, swift, staring wights,
   What is't ye do? What life lead? eh, dull goggles?
How do ye vary your vile days and nights?
   How pass your Sundays? Are ye still but joggles
In ceaseless wash? Still nought but gapes, and bites,
   And drinks, and stares, diversified with boggles?

A FISH ANSWERS

Amazing monster! that, for aught I know,
   With the first sight of thee didst make our race
   For ever stare! O flat and shocking face,
Grimly divided from the breast below!
Thou that on dry land horribly dost go
   With a split body and most ridiculous pace,
   Prong after prong, disgracer of all grace,
Long-useless-finned, haired, upright, unwet, slow!

O breather of unbreathable, sword-sharp air,
   How canst exist? How bear thyself, thou dry
And dreary sloth? What particle canst share
   Of the only blessed life, the watery?
I sometimes see of ye an actual *pair*
   Go by! linked fin by fin! most odiously.

LEIGH HUNT

OLD MOTHER MINCHIN

Old Mother Minchin
When she was wed
Wanted to live
In a watercress bed.

Straw to sit on,
And reeds to press,
There she sat
In her Sunday dress!

What a peculiar
Thing to do!
But old Mother Minchin
Wasn't like you:

With a feather as strong
As a fine quill pen—
Old Mother Minchin,
My little moor hen!

JEAN KENWARD

KING DAVID AND KING SOLOMON

King David and King Solomon
   Led merry, merry lives,
With many, many lady friends
   And many, many wives;
But when old age crept over them,
   With many, many qualms,
King Solomon wrote the Proverbs,
   And King David wrote the Psalms.

J. B. NAYLOR

THE JUMBLIES

I

They went to sea in a Sieve, they did,
    In a Sieve they went to sea:
In spite of all their friends could say,
On a winter's morn, on a stormy day,
    In a Sieve they went to sea!
And when the Sieve turned round and round,
And everyone cried, "You'll all be drowned!"
They called aloud, "Our Sieve ain't big,
But we don't care a button! we don't care a fig!
    In a Sieve we'll go to sea!"
        Far and few, far and few,
        Their heads are green, and their hands are blue,
            Are the lands where the Jumblies live;
            And they went to sea in a Sieve.

II

They sailed away in a Sieve, they did,
    In a Sieve they sailed so fast,
With only a beautiful pea-green veil
Tied with a riband by way of a sail,
    To a small tobacco-pipe mast;
And everyone said, who saw them go,
"O won't they be soon upset, you know!
For the sky is dark, and the voyage is long,
And happen what may, it's extremely wrong
    In a Sieve to sail so fast!"
        Far and few, far and few,
            Are the lands where the Jumblies live;
        Their heads are green, and their hands are blue,
            And they went to sea in a Sieve.

III

The water it soon came in, it did,
    The water it soon came in;
So to keep them dry, they wrapped their feet
In a pinky paper all folded neat,
    And they fastened it down with a pin.
And they passed the night in a crockery-jar,
And each of them said, "How wise we are!
Though the sky be dark, and the voyage be long,
Yet we never can think we were rash or wrong,
    While round in our Sieve we spin!"
        Far and few, far and few,
           Are the lands where the Jumblies live;
         Their heads are green, and their hands are blue,
           And they went to sea in a Sieve.

IV

And all night long they sailed away;
    And when the sun went down,
They whistled and warbled a moony song
To the echoing sound of a coppery gong,
In the shade of the mountains brown.
"O Timballo! How happy we are,
When we live in a sieve and a crockery-jar,
And all night long in the moonlight pale,
We sail away with a pea-green sail,
    In the shade of the mountains brown!"
        Far and few, far and few,
           Are the lands where the Jumblies live;
         Their heads are green, and their hands are blue,
           And they went to sea in a Sieve.

V

They sailed to the Western Sea, they did,
  To a land all covered with trees,
And they bought an Owl, and a useful Cart,
And a pound of Rice, and a Cranbery Tart,
  And a hive of silvery Bees.
And they bought a Pig, and some green Jack-daws,
And a lovely Monkey with lollipop paws,
And forty bottles of Ringo-Bo-Ree,
  And no end of Stilton Cheese.
    Far and few, far and few,
      Are the lands where the Jumblies live;
      Their heads are green, and their hands are blue,
      And they went to sea in a Sieve.

VI

And in twenty years they all came back,
  In twenty years or more,
And everyone said, "How tall you've grown!
For they've been to the Lakes, and the Terrible Zone,
  And the hills of the Chankly Bore;"
And they drank their health, and gave them a feast
Of dumplings made of beautiful yeast;
And everyone said, "If we only live,
We too will go to sea in a Sieve,—
  To the hills of the Chankly Bore!"
    Far and few, far and few,
      Are the lands where the Jumblies live;
      Their heads are green, and their hands are blue,
      And they went to sea in a Sieve.

EDWARD LEAR

A SONG ABOUT MYSELF

I

There was a naughty Boy,
    A naughty boy was he,
He would not stop at home,
    He could not quiet be—
        He took
        In his Knapsack
        A Book
        Full of vowels
        And a shirt
        With some towels
        A slight cap
        For night cap—
        A hair brush,
        Comb ditto,
        New Stockings
        For old ones
        Would split O!
        This Knapsack
        Tight at's back
        He rivetted close
And followèd his Nose
    To the North,
    To the North,
And follow'd his nose
    To the North.

II

There was a naughty boy
    And a naughty boy was he,
For nothing would he do
    But scribble poetry—

He took
An ink stand
In his hand
And a pen
Big as ten
In the other.
And away
In a Pother
He ran
To the mountains
And fountains
And ghostes
And Postes
And witches
And ditches
And wrote
In his coat
When the weather
Was cool,
Fear of gout,
And without,
When the weather
Was warm—
Och the charm
When we choose
To follow one's nose
To the north,
To the north,
To follow one's nose
To the north!

III

There was a naughty boy
    And a naughty boy was he,
He kept little fishes
    In washing tubs three
        In spite
        Of the might
        Of the Maid
        Nor afraid
        Of his Granny-good—
        He often would
        Hurly burly
        Get up early
        And go
        By hook or crook
        To the brook
        And bring home
        Miller's thumb
        Tittlebat
        Not over fat,
        Minnows small
        As the stall
        Of a glove,
        Not above
        The size
        Of a nice
        Little Baby's
        Little fingers—
        O he made
        'Twas his trade
    Of Fish a pretty Kettle
        A Kettle—

A Kettle
Of Fish a pretty Kettle
A Kettle!

IV

There was a naughty Boy,
And a naughty Boy was he,
He ran away to Scotland
The people for to see—
Then he found
That the ground
Was as hard,
That a yard
Was as long,
That a song,
Was as merry,
That a cherry
Was as red—
That lead
Was as weighty,
That fourscore
Was as eighty,
That a door
Was as wooden
As in England—
So he stood in his shoes
And he wonder'd,
He wonder'd,
He stood in his shoes
And he wonder'd.

JOHN KEATS

PLACES,
WEATHERS,
CREATURES,
THINGS

BOYS AND GIRLS
COME OUT TO PLAY

Boys and girls come out to play
The moon doth shine as bright as day.
Leave your supper and leave your sleep
And join your playfellows in the street.
Come with a whoop and come with a call
Come with a good will or not at all.
Up the ladder and down the wall
A half-penny loaf will serve us all;
You find milk and I'll find flour,
And we'll have a pudding in half an hour.

ANON

DECEMBER

Frost is the quietest thing that grows
All in a night it comes to leaf
And flower more perfect than the rose
—So firm its stem and yet so brief.
Its seed is quite invisible
Its passing smells not of decay
When in the light the mutable
Thin petals quietly pass away,

Then leave no trace but the brown stain
To show where they had sustenance,
They shed no faded whispering train
Of dead leaves in the wind to dance.
Are they compounded only of light
And dying mingle with their source?
Snow in its birth is even as white
But dies with tears and slow remorse,

Less crystal than these fragile spires
Fading like insubstantial ghost
Into the sun's new-kindled fires
That fuse their gold with silver frost.

T. W. RAMSEY

THE SNOW

In no way that I chose to go
Could I escape the falling snow.

I shut my eyes, wet with my fears:
The snow still whispered at my ears.

Snow was my comrade, snow my fate,
In a country huge and desolate.

My footsteps made a shallow space,
And then the snow filled up the place.

And all the walking I had done
Was on a journey not begun.

I did not know the distance gone,
But resolutely travelled on,

While silently on every hand
Fell the sorrow of the land,

And no way that I chose to go
Could lead me from the grief of snow.

                    CLIFFORD DYMENT

VISTA

The snow,
Ah, yes; ah, yes, indeed,
Is white and beautiful, white and beautiful,
Verily beautiful—
From my window.
The sea,
As, yes; ah, yes, indeed,
Is green and alluring, green and alluring,
Verily alluring—
From the shore.
Love?—
Ah, yes, ah, yes; ah, yes, indeed,
Verily yes, ah yes, indeed!

ALFRED KREYMBORG

SOMETHING TOLD THE WILD GEESE

Something told the wild geese
It was time to go,
Though the fields lay golden
Something whispered, "Snow!"
Leaves were green and stirring,
Berries lustre-glossed,
But beneath warm feathers
Something cautioned, "Frost!"

All the sagging orchards
Steamed with amber spice,
But each wild beast stiffened
At remembered ice.
Something told the wild geese
It was time to fly—
Summer sun was on their wings,
Winter in their cry.

RACHEL FIELD

WINTER

(with very little money in a great city)

There's snow in every street
Where I go up and down,
And there's no woman, man or dog
That knows me in the town.

I know each shop, and all
These Jews and Russian Poles,
For I go walking night and noon
To spare my sack of coals.

J. M. SYNGE

SLOW SPRING

A bitter wind cuts down the daffodils.
The yellow sun goes down after the gales.
Smaller than matchheads are the buds on thorns.
They will not flare before the weather turns.

One twig of blossom on a half dead tree.
One peewit dives and swerves with his spring cry.
One old man in his cottage, living alone,
Looks out, stays in. Another day is gone.

SYDNEY TREMAYNE

GAY COMES THE SINGER

Gay comes the singer
    With a song,
Sing we all together,
    All things young;
Field and wood and fallow,
    Lark at dawn,
Young rooks cawing, cawing,
    Philomel
Still complaining of the ancient wrong.

Twitters now the swallow,
    Swans are shrill
Still remembering sorrow,
Cuckoo, cuckoo, goes the cuckoo calling
    On the wooded hill.

The birds sing fair,
    Singing earth,
Gracious after travail
    Of new birth,
Lies in radiant light,
    Fragrant air.

Broad spreads the lime,
    Bough and leaf.
Underfoot the thyme,
    Green the turf.
Here come the dances
    In the grass

Running water glances,
    Murmurs past.

Happy is the place,
  Whispering
Through the open weather
Blow the winds of spring.

(from the manuscript of Benedictbeuern
translated by Helen Waddell)

THE THRUSH'S NEST

Within a thick and spreading hawthorn bush
  That overhung a mole-hill large and round,
I heard from morn to morn a merry thrush
  Sing hymns to sunrise, while I drank the sound
With joy; and, often an intruding guest,
  I watched her secret toils from day to day—
How true she warped the moss to form a nest,
  And modelled it within with wood and clay;
And by and by, like heath-bells gilt with dew,
  There lay her shining eggs, as bright as flowers,
Ink-spotted over shells of greeny blue;
  And there I witnessed, in the sunny hours,
A brood of nature's minstrels chirp and fly,
Glad as that sunshine and the laughing sky.

JOHN CLARE

THE FIRST SPRING MORNING

Look! Look! the spring is come:
 O feel the gentle air,
That wanders thro' the boughs to burst
 The thick buds everywhere!
 The birds are glad to see
 The high unclouded sun:
Winter is fled away, they sing,
 The gay time is begun.

 Adown the meadows green
 Let us go dance and play,
And look for violets in the lane,
 And ramble far away
 To gather primroses,
 That in the woodlands grow,
And hunt for oxlips, or if yet
 The blades of bluebells show.

 There the old woodman gruff
 Hath half the coppice cut,
And weaves the hurdles all day long
 Beside his willow hut.
 We'll steal on him, and then
 Startle him, all with glee
Singing our song of winter fled
 And summer soon to be.

ROBERT BRIDGES

KEEPER'S WOOD

Within these dusky woods
The blackthorn hides.
The violets in the rides
On a grey day
Among pale primrose-buds
Crouch, hidden away.

A loud jay curses all.
A gust goes by
Under the cloud-cold sky,
And as you walk,
In the fields the lambs call,
And the rooks talk.

How pale it is, the sky
That sheds its peace
On the violets like a fleece,
And yellow buds,
While the lambs feebly cry
Outside the woods.

F. T. PRINCE

THE FERNS

High, high in the branches
the seawinds plunge and roar.
A storm is moving westward,
but here on the forest floor
the ferns have captured stillness.
A green sea growth they are.

The ferns lie underwater
in a light of the forest's green.
Their motion is like stillness,
as if water shifts between
and a great storm quivers
through fathoms of green.

GENE BARO

GIANT THUNDER

Giant Thunder, striding home,
Wonders if his supper's done.

"Hag wife, hag wife, bring me bones!"
"They are not done," the old hag moans.

"Not done? not done?" the giant roars,
And heaves the old wife out of doors.

Cries he, "I'll have them, cooked or not!"
And overturns the cooking pot.

He flings the burning coals about;
See how the lightning flashes out!

Upon the gale the old hag rides,
The clouded moon for terror hides.

All the world with thunder quakes;
Forest shudders, mountain shakes;

From the cloud the rainstorm breaks;
Village ponds are turned to lakes;
Every living creature wakes.

Hungry giant, lie you still!
Stamp no more from hill to hill—
Tomorrow you shall have your fill.

                              JAMES REEVES

WEATHERS

I

This is the weather the cuckoo likes,
    And so do I;
When showers betumble the chestnut spikes,
    And nestlings fly:
And the little brown nightingale bills his best,
And they sit outside at "The Traveller's Rest",
And maids come forth sprig-muslin drest,
And citizens dream of the south and west,
    And so do I.

II

This is the weather the shepherd shuns,
    And so do I;
When beeches drip in browns and duns,
    And thresh, and ply;
And hill-hid tides throb, throe on throe,
And meadow rivulets overflow,
And drops on gate-bars hang in a row,
And rooks in families homeward go,
    And so do I.

THOMAS HARDY

THE OUSEL COCK

The ousel cock so black of hue,
 With orange-tawny bill,
The throstle with his note so true,
 The wren with little quill; .

The finch, the sparrow, and the lark,
 The plain-song cuckoo gray,
Whose note full many a man doth mark,
 And dares not answer nay.

     WILLIAM SHAKESPEARE
   (*from* A Midsummer Night's Dream)

THE BARN OWL

While moonlight, silvering all the walls,
Through every mouldering crevice falls,
Tipping with white his powdery plume,
As shades or shifts the changing gloom;
The Owl that, watching in the barn,
Sees the mouse creeping in the corn,
Sits still and shuts his round blue eyes
As if he slept—until he spies
The little beast within his stretch—
Then starts—and seizes on the wretch!

     SAMUEL BUTLER

SPRING SONG

Ho starling, quarrelsome swaggerer, you up there on
    the gable,
Are you seeing and hearing the first little signs of
    spring?
We huddled winterbound stragglers, well-accustomed
    to hardship
See you cocking your eye at a prospect that makes you
    sing.

O starling, ramshackle whistler, all unkempt in your
    speckles,
You swoop down your scale of notes like a child on a
    slide
Then scooping, excelsior slitherer, poise again for the
    downswoop:
Grateful we are that you take us along for the ride,

And grateful, faithful old sojourner, most of all for
    your staying
When others flew south to the sun and the colour and
    heat.
Oh starling, darling, give us the high sign—
Tell us the spring can be seen from the end of the
    street!

JOAN MURRAY SIMPSON

I AM TIRED OF THE WIND

I am tired of the wind leaning against me,
　　Let it lean somewhere else!
On a brick wall that is too insensible to care,
　　Or the trees on the common.

Why should it shove me and elbow me?
　　It is too familiar!
I will lure it to the cliff edge, then jump aside
　　For it to plunge over.

There! Now it screams down, flailing the sea;
　　Smashes on rocks.
Grass does not stir across fields, smoke blur above
　　chimneys.
Oh, but suddenly I am afraid!

If the wind is a God's breath and I've murdered the
　　wind,
　　Will not that dead giant
More terrible then than in his platinum waking day
　　Snort gustily in my dreams?

JOHN SMITH

BIRDS MUST SING

Comes the time of leaves breaking,
    Birds, they must sing;
Lightly sleeping, early waking,
    Must, must sing;
However long the waiting
Until the cold's abating,
Through sudden brume and sleeting,
    Birds must sing!

Comes the time of first courting,
    Birds, they must sing;
All flirting, all disporting,
    Must, must sing:
In quarrelling and teasing,
With ardour all increasing,
At last the full heart's easing—
    Birds must sing!

Comes the time of nest-building,
    Birds, they must sing;
Straw-saving, leaf-wielding,
    Must, must sing;
And when the nest is fashioned,
On boughs above it stationed,
Elated and impassioned,
    Birds must sing!

ANTHONY RYE

THE COW

The friendly cow all red and white,
   I love with all my heart:
She gives me cream with all her might,
   To eat with apple tart.

She wanders lowing here and there,
   And yet she cannot stray,
All in the pleasant open air,
   The pleasant light of day;

And blown by all the winds that pass
   And wet with all the showers,
She walks among the meadow grass
   And eats the meadow flowers.

ROBERT LOUIS STEVENSON

THE BAT

By day the bat is cousin to the mouse.
He likes the attic of an aging house.

His fingers make a hat about his head.
His pulse beat is so slow we think him dead.

He loops in crazy figures half the night
Among the trees that face the corner light.

But when he brushes up against a screen,
We are afraid of what our eyes have seen;

For something is amiss or out of place
When mice with wings can wear a human face

THEODORE ROETHKE

SONG

*(To Mademoiselle Teresita Guillen
playing her piano of six notes)*

The he-lizard is crying.
The she-lizard is crying.

The he-lizard and the she-lizard
with little white aprons.

Have lost without wanting to
their wedding ring.

Ah, their little leaden wedding ring,
'ah, their little ring of lead!

A large sky without people
carries the birds in its balloon.

The sun, rotund captain,
wears a satin waistcoat.

Look how old they are!
How old the lizards are!

Oh, how they cry and cry,
Oh! Oh! How they go on crying.

FEDERICO GARCIA LORCA
*(translated by J. L. Gili
and Stephen Spender)*

RABBITS

Rabbits have fur
And also more rabbits
And it is a habit.

A habit is something you are doing
Over and over again
Because you are liking it
When you have it.

A habit of rabbits is having more.
First there is a rabbit with fur
and you have it.
But soon there are more.

Soon they are having more rabbits
Over and over again and liking to do it
And then it is a habit
And rabbits really have it.

RAY FABRIZIO

EYES ARE LIT UP

Someone whom no man can see
Is lighting candles in the tree.

Star by star, on every bough
There is a taper burning now.

Quietly the forest through,
Eyes are lit up, two by two.

The silky moles and velvet mice
Have eyes as sharp as cracks in ice.

Dark lanterns of the owls begin
To burn like emeralds and sin.

The raccoon built of hidden wire
Prowls by the glow of his brain fire.

Herons stand as still as years
And see the fish swim through their tears.

All the creatures of the night
Are busy being their own light.

ROBERT P. TRISTRAM COFFIN

from *SONG OF MYSELF*

I think I could turn and live with animals, they are so
    placid and self-contained;
I stand and look at them long and long.
They do not sweat and whine about their condition;
They do not lie awake in the dark and weep for their
    sins;
They do not make me sick discussing their duty to
    God;
Not one is dissatisfied—not one is demented with the
    mania of owning things;
Not one kneels to another, nor to his kind that lived
    thousands of years ago;
Not one is respectable or industrious over the whole
    earth.

WALT WHITMAN

WORDS

The word bites like a fish.
Shall I throw it back free
Arrowing to that sea
Where thoughts lash tail and fin?
Or shall I pull it in
To rhyme upon a dish?

STEPHEN SPENDER

THE SNARE

I hear a sudden cry of pain!
  There is a rabbit in a snare:
Now I hear the cry again,
  But I cannot tell from where.

But I cannot tell from where
  He is calling out for aid;
Crying on the frightened air,
  Making everything afraid.

Making everything afraid,
  Wrinkling up his little face,
As he cries again for aid;
  And I cannot find the place!

And I cannot find the place
  Where his paw is in the snare:
Little one! Oh, little one!
  I am searching everywhere.

JAMES STEPHENS

MILK FOR THE CAT

When the tea is brought at five o'clock,
And all the neat curtains are drawn with care,
The little black cat with bright green eyes
Is suddenly purring there.

At first she pretends, having nothing to do,
She has come in merely to blink by the grate,
But, though tea may be late or the milk may be sour
She is never late.

And presently her agate eyes
Take a soft, large, milky haze
And her independent casual glance
Becomes a stiff, hard gaze.

Then she stamps her claws or lofts her ears,
Or twists her tail and begins to stir,
Till suddenly all her lithe body becomes
One breathing, trembling purr.

The children eat and wriggle and laugh,
The two old ladies stroke their silk;
But the cat is grown small and thin with desire,
Transformed to a creeping lust for milk.

The white saucer like some full moon descends
At last from the clouds of the table above;
She sighs and dreams and thrills and glows,
Transfigured with love.

She nestles over the shining rim,
Buries her chin in the creamy sea;
Her tail hangs loose; each drowsy paw
Is doubled under each bending knee.

A long, dim ecstasy holds her life;
Her world is an infinite shapeless white,
Till her tongue has curled the last holy drop,
Then she sinks back into the night,

Draws and dips her body to heap
Her sleepy nerves in the great arm-chair,
Lies defeated and buried deep
Three or four hours unconscious there.

HAROLD MONRO

MACAVITY: THE MYSTERY CAT

Macavity's a Mystery Cat: he's called the Hidden Paw—
For he's the master criminal who can defy the Law.
He's the bafflement of Scotland Yard, the Flying
    Squad's despair:
For when they reach the scene of crime—Macavity's
    not there!

Macavity, Macavity, there's no one like Macavity,
He's broken every human law, he breaks the law of
    gravity.
His powers of levitation would make a fakir stare,
And when you reach the scene of crime—Macavity's
    not there!
You may seek him in the basement, you may look up
    in the air—
But I tell you once and once again, Macavity's not
    there!

Macavity's a ginger cat, he's very tall and thin;
You would know him if you saw him, for his eyes are
    sunken in.
His brow is deeply lined with thought, his head is
    highly domed;
His coat is dusty from neglect, his whiskers are un-
    combed.
He sways his head from side to side, with movements
    like a snake;
And when you think he's half asleep, he's always wide
    awake.

Macavity, Macavity, there's no one like Macavity,
For he's a fiend in feline shape, a monster of depravity.

———

You may meet him in a by-street, you may see him in
    the square—
But when a crime's discovered, then Macavity's not
    there!

He's outwardly respectable. (They say he cheats at
    cards.)
And his footprints are not found in any file of Scotland
    Yard's.
And when the larder's looted, or the jewel-case is
    rifled,
Or when the milk is missing, or another Peke's been
    stifled,
Or the greenhouse glass is broken, and the trellis past
    repair—
Ay, there's the wonder of the thing! Macavity's not
    there!

And when the Foreign Office finds a Treaty's gone
    astray,
Or the Admiralty lose some plans and drawings by the
    way,
There may be a scrap of paper in the hall or on the
    stair—
But it's useless to investigate—Macavity's not there!
And when the loss has been disclosed, the Secret
    Service say:
"It must have been Macavity!"—but he's a mile away,
You'll be sure to find him resting, or a-licking of his
    thumbs,
Or engaged in doing complicated long division sums.

Macavity, Macavity, there's no one like Macavity,
There never was a Cat of such deceitfulness and
    suavity.

He always has an alibi, and one or two to spare:
At whatever time the deed took place—MACAVITY
    WASN'T THERE!
And they say that all the Cats whose wicked deeds are
    widely known
(I might mention Mungojerrie, I might mention Grid-
    dlebone)
Are nothing more than agents for the Cat who all the
    time
Just controls their operations: the Napoleon of Crime!

T. S. ELIOT

CIRCUS HAND

All my life long
   Since I was thirteen,
Loved like St. Francis
   Is what I would have been.

The fish still scatter,
   The pony shies,
The snake bites
   And the bird flies.

Yet here is one who is
   What I would have been
All my life long;
   And he is thirteen.

PAUL DEHN

THE BOY

I'd like, above all, to be one of those
Who drive with wild black horses through the night,
torches like hair uplifted in affright
when the great wind of their wild hunting blows.
I'd like to stand in front as in a boat,
tall, like a long floating flag unrolled.
And dark, but with a helmet made of gold,
restlessly flashing. And behind to ride
ten other looming figures side by side,
with helmets all unstable like my own,
now clear like glass, now old and blank like stone.
And one to stand by me and blow us space
with the brass trumpet that can blaze and blare,
blowing a black solitude through which we tear
like dreams that speed too fast to leave a trace.
Houses behind us fall upon their knees,
alleys cringe crookedly before our train,
squares in flight; we summon and we seize:
we ride, and our great horses rush like rain.

RAINER MARIA RILKE
(*translated by J. B. Leishman*)

THE ELEPHANT
KNOCKED THE GROUND

The elephant knocked the ground with a stick,
He knocked it slow, he knocked it quick.
He knocked it till his trunk turned black—
Then the ground turned round and knocked him back.

ADRIAN MITCHELL

BIRDS

A bird flies and has wings
And it certainly sings

A bird when it sings is always certain.
It sings and sings about certain things,
Like flying and having wings
Or being only a bird in a tree
And free

Free is when you are being certain
And wanting to sing certainly
About certain things.

A bird is free and certainly sings.
It sings and sings about flying and having wings
Or being always a certain thing
When it is only a bird in a tree
Singing certainly
And free.

RAY FABRIZIO

THE BIRD-MAN

Man is a bird:
    He rises on fine wings
Into the Heaven's clear light;
    He flies away and sings—
There's music in his flight.

Man is a bird:
    In swiftest speed he burns,
With twist and dive and leap;
    A bird whose sudden turns
Can drive the frightened sheep.

Man is a bird:
    Over the mountain high,
Whose head is in the skies,
    Cut from its shoulder by
A cloud—the bird-man flies.

Man is a bird:
    Eagles from mountain crag
Swooped down to prove his worth;
    But *now* they *rise* to drag
Him down from Heaven to Earth!

W. H. DAVIES

HOW TO PAINT
THE PORTRAIT OF A BIRD

First paint a cage
with an open door
then paint
something pretty
something simple
something fine
something useful
for the bird
next place the canvas against a tree
in a garden
in a wood
or in a forest
hide behind the tree
without speaking
without moving . . .
Sometimes the bird comes quickly
but it can also take many years
before making up its mind
Don't be discouraged
wait
wait if necessary for years
the quickness or the slowness of the coming
of the bird having no relation
to the success of the picture
When the bird comes
if it comes
observe the deepest silence
wait for the bird to enter the cage
and when it has entered
gently close the door with the paint-brush

then
one by one paint out all the bars
taking care not to touch one feather of the bird
Next make a portrait of the tree
choosing the finest of its branches
for the bird
paint also the green leaves and the freshness of the wind
dust in the sun
and the sound of the grazing cattle in the heat of
 summer
and wait for the bird to decide to sing
If the bird does not sing
it is a bad sign
a sign that the picture is bad
but if it sings it is a good sign
a sign that you are ready to sign
so then you pluck very gently
one of the quills of the bird
and you write your name in the corner of the picture.

JACQUES PREVERT
(*translated by Paul Dehn*)

JENNY WREN FELL SICK

Jenny Wren fell sick
  Upon a merry time,
In came Robin Redbreast
  And brought her sops and wine.

Eat well of the sop, Jenny,
  Drink well of the wine.
Thank you, Robin, kindly,
  You shall be mine.

Jenny Wren got well,
  And stood upon her feet;
And told Robin plainly,
  She loved him not a bit.

Robin he got angry,
  And hopped upon a twig,
Saying, Out upon you, Fie upon you!
  Bold faced jig!

NURSERY RHYME

PIGEONS

They paddle with staccato feet
In powder-pools of sunlight,
Small blue busybodies
Strutting like fat gentlemen
With hands clasped
Under their swallowtail coats;
And, as they stump about,
Their heads like tiny hammers
Tap at imaginary nails
In non-existent walls.
Elusive ghosts of sunshine
Slither down the green gloss
Of their necks an instant, and are gone.

Summer hangs drugged from sky to earth
In limpid fathoms of silence:
Only warm dark dimples of sound
Slide like slow bubbles
From the contented throats.

Raise a casual hand—
With one quick gust
They fountain into air.

RICHARD KELL

171

TELEGRAPH POLES

These, in the dusk, are bars
    On the lit score of spring,
When early-comer stars
    Lean outward, listening.

Rams to the music muster
    Their horned and tenor herds
Where, on a wire stave, cluster
    The semi-quaver birds.

PAUL DEHN

LOVELIEST OF TREES

Loveliest of trees, the cherry now
Is hung with bloom along the bough,
And stands about the woodland ride
Wearing white for Eastertide.

Now, of my threescore years and ten,
Twenty will not come again,
And take from seventy springs a score,
It only leaves me fifty more.

And since to look at things in bloom
Fifty springs is little room,
About the woodlands I will go
To see the cherry hung with snow.

A. E. HOUSMAN

TWO SPARROWS

Two sparrows, feeding,
heard a thrush
sing to the dawn.
the first said, "Tush!

In all my life
I never heard
a more affected
singing bird."

The second said,
"It's you and me,
who slave to keep
the likes of he."

"And if we cared,"
both sparrows said,
"we'd do that singing
on our head."

The thrush pecked sideways
and was dumb.
"And now," they screamed,
"he's pinched our crumb!"

HUMBERT WOLFE

MORNING GLORY

Morning glory
  Cool jewels
    Shade!

More blue than grottoes
  Blue than breeze,

Pools like pools
  In pools of leaves,

Cool my eyes
  And copper days.

Eyes in dew
  Where jewels graze,

Mosaics where
  The sky is fetched

Broken blue
  Where glass is matched;

Ice is satin
  Ice is stretched:

Blue dew,
  Cool jewels,
    Shade!

                    PAUL ROCHE

———
174

THE STORM

There came a wind like a bugle;
It quivered through the grass,
And a green chill upon the heat
So ominous did pass
We barred the windows and the doors
As from an emerald ghost;
The doom's electric moccasin
That very instant passed.
On a strange mob of panting trees,
And fences fled away,
And rivers where the houses ran
The living looked that day.
The bell within the steeple wild
The flying tidings whirled.
How much can come
And much can go,
And yet abide the world!

EMILY DICKINSON

WAVES AGAINST A DOG

Had I had the power I would have stretched
that wave on this rock and bitten it. But now
I have to thrust a jaw at this foam. Salting
my teeth, adultering my saliva. And my teeth
get hold of just nothing, just whiteness and sun.

Afraid? Not I. Not of this salty anger. I have
killed a lot in my life. Not frightened. Not I.
But nothing to my teeth, just touch and goes
this big blue wave. Afraid of me. Circles my feet.
Vanishes. Must catch before it breaks on the rock.

Dive. What strength! I'm hurled back to the rock,
whirling round, looking at the hill, not the sea.
Dive again. A large blue tongue shows me
the pattern of the rocks, puts me on my feet,
there. Soaked. If only I had teeth. If only.

To bite this blueness to pieces, to pierce this
blue big belly, take my revenge, bite—If.
But now I cannot even touch: the salt teases me.
I look around: always the white foam. And I bark.
I bark while the rock ducks under another wave.

TANER BAYBARS

LEISURE

What is this life if, full of care,
We have no time to stand and stare?

No time to stand beneath the boughs
And stare as long as sheep or cows.

No time to see, when woods we pass,
Where squirrels hide their nuts in grass.

No time to see, in broad daylight,
Streams full of stars, like skies at night.

No time to turn at beauty's glance,
And watch her feet, how they can dance.

No time to wait till her mouth can
Enrich that smile her eyes began.

A poor life this if, full of care,
We have no time to stand and stare.

W. H. DAVIES

TAILOR'S SONG

Swing low, sweet sun, like a gold hunter
Waistcoat-high in the lavender light;
Consulted, slipped from a gloved finger
Into the pocket of night.

Spin high, sweet moon, in the cold winter,
Latchet-low beyond window-bars,
Wheel of a sewing machine, my Singer
Under the thimble stars.

PAUL DEHN

TWINKLE TWINKLE LITTLE STAR

Twinkle, twinkle, little star,
How I wonder what you are!
Up above the world so high,
Like a diamond in the sky.

When the blazing sun is gone,
When he nothing shines upon,
Then you show your little light,
Twinkle, twinkle all the night.

Then the traveller in the dark,
Thanks you for your tiny spark,
He could not see which way to go
If you did not twinkle so.

In the dark blue sky you keep,
And often through my curtains peep,
For you never shut your eye,
'Til the sun is in the sky.

As your bright and tiny spark
Lights the traveller in the dark—
Though I know not what you are,
Twinkle, twinkle, little star.

JANE TAYLOR

HARVEST HOME

The wagons loom like blue caravans in the dusk;
They lumber mysteriously down the moonlit lanes.

We ride on the stacks of rust gold corn,
Filling the sky with our song.

The horses toss their heads and the harness-bells
Jingle all the way.

HERBERT READ

THE GNATS

The gnats are dancing in the sun,
In vibrant needles of light they run
On the air, and hover in noiseless sound,
Ecstasy ballet, round and around,
Soon for human body bound.

The pin-thin slivers, wingy, white,
Whirl in restless, passionate flight—
Zooming atoms circling, twisting,
Darting, jiving,
Target-diving.
In orbit on orbit of dazzle-gold light,
The gnats are limbering up to bite.

ODETTE TCHERNINE

A CARRION CROW SAT ON AN OAK

A carrion crow sat on an oak,
Watching a tailor shape his cloak;
Wife, cried he, bring me my bow,
That I may shoot yon carrion crow.

The tailor shot and missed his mark,
And shot his own sow through the heart;
Wife, bring brandy in a spoon,
For our poor sow is in a swoon.

NURSERY RHYME

TO A STARVED HARE IN
THE GARDEN IN WINTER

Soft-footed stroller from the herbless wood,
Stealing so mutely through my garden ground,
I will not balk thine eager quest for food,
Nor take thy life, nor startle thee with sound.
I spared the wanton squirrel, though I saw
His autumn raid upon my nuts and cones;
I spared his frisky brush and bushy jaw;
And shall I wound the poor disheartened ones?
Come freely: in my heart thy charter lies;
Feed boldly—what thou gain'st I cannot lose.
When robin shuffles on the snow-white sill,
We serve his winsome hunger; who would choose
To daunt his ruddy breast and wistful eyes?
But, hare or robin, it is hunger still.

CHARLES TENNYSON TURNER

HIE AWAY

Hie away, hie away,
Over bank, over brae,
Where the copsewood is the greenest,
Where the fountains glisten sheenest,
Where the lady-fern grows strongest,
Where the morning dew lies longest,
Where the black-cock sweetest sips it,
Where the fairy latest trips it:
Hie to haunts right seldom seen,
Lovely, lonesome, cool, and green,
Over bank and over brae,
Hie away, hie away.

SIR WALTER SCOTT

THE BOY FISHING

I am cold and alone,
On my tree-root sitting as still as stone.
The fish come to my net. I scorned the sun,
The voices on the road, and they have gone.
My eyes are buried in the cold pond, under
The cold, spread leaves; my thoughts are silver-wet.
I have ten stickleback, a half-day's plunder,
Safe in my jar. I shall have ten more yet.

E. J. SCOVELL

MUSHROOMS

Overnight, very
Whitely, discreetly,
Very quietly

Our toes, our noses
Take hold of the loam,
Acquire the air.

Nobody sees us,
Stops us, betrays us;
The small grains make room.

Soft fists insist on
Heaving the needles,
The leafy bedding,

Even the paving;
Our hammers, our rams,
Earless and eyeless.

Perfectly voiceless,
Widen the crannies,
Shoulder through holes. We

Diet on water,
On crumbs of shadow,
Bland-mannered, asking

Little or nothing.
So many of us!
So many of us!

We are shelves, we are
Tables, we are meek,
We are edible,

Nudgers and shovers
In spite of ourselves.
Our kind multiplies;

We shall by morning
Inherit the earth.
Our foot's in the door.

SYLVIA PLATH

185

BOY INTO HERON

High on a stilt-raised bed above the reeds
He lay and watched the birds, saw the grey heron come,
Perched like himself on long stiff legs,
To search the mud wet shore for frogs and fish,
Marked his grey plumage and the deep slate tail,
And the dark coronet of glossy plumes,
And watching so intently, lost himself,
His own identity merged in the bird's.
And when the heron rose above the lough,
His long legs arrowed in the wind,
His plumes laid flat, the boy took wings,
And rose with him and skimmed across the lake,
And knew the majesty and joy of flight.
Not till the heron grew a distant speck
Beyond his sight, did he, reluctant creep
Into his body's wingless form again.

CELIA RANDALL

ARIZONA NATURE MYTH

Up in the heavenly saloon
Sheriff sun and rustler moon
Gamble, stuck in the sheriff's mouth
The fag end of an afternoon.

There in the bad town of the sky
Sheriff, nervy, wonders why
He's let himself wander so far West
On his own; he looks with a smoky eye

At the rustler opposite turning white,
Lays down a king for Law, sits tight
Bluffing. On it that crooked moon
Plays an ace and shoots for the light.

Spurs, badge, and uniform red,
(It looks like blood, but he's shamming dead).
Down drops the marshal, and under cover
Crawls out dogwise, ducking his head.

But Law that don't get its man ain't Law.
Next day, faster on the draw,
Sheriff creeping up from the other side,
Blazes his way in through the back door.

But moon's not there. He's ridden out on
A galloping phenomenon,
A wonder horse, quick as light.
Moon's left town. Moon's clean gone.

JAMES MICHIE

I WANDERED LONELY AS A CLOUD

I wandered lonely as a cloud
That floats on high o'er vales and hills,
When all at once I saw a crowd,
A host, of golden daffodils;
Beside the lake, beneath the trees,
Fluttering and dancing in the breeze.

Continuous as the stars that shine
And twinkle on the milky way,
They stretched in never-ending line
Along the margin of a bay:
Ten thousand saw I at a glance,
Tossing their heads in sprightly dance.

The waves beside them danced; but they
Out-did the sparkling waves in glee:
A poet could not but be gay,
In such a jocund company:
I gazed—and gazed—but little thought
What wealth the show to me had brought:

For oft, when on my couch I lie
In vacant or in pensive mood,
They flash upon that inward eye
Which is the bliss of solitude;
And then my heart with pleasure fills,
And dances with the daffodils.

WILLIAM WORDSWORTH

STUFF AND NONSENSE

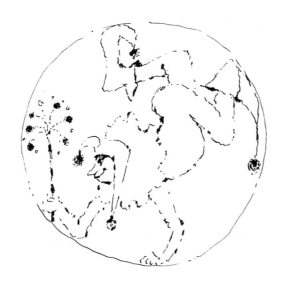

STUFF

Lovers lie around in it.
Broken glass is found in it
Grass
I like that stuff

Tuna fish get trapped in it
Legs come wrapped in it
Nylon
I like that stuff

Eskimos and tramps chew it
Madame Tussaud gave status to it
Wax
I like that stuff

Elephants get sprayed with it
Scotch is made with it
Water
I like that stuff

Clergy are dumbfounded by it
Bones are surrounded by it
Flesh
I like that stuff

Harps are strung with it
Mattresses are sprung with it
Wire
I like that stuff

Carpenters make cots of it
Undertakers use lots of it
Wood
I like that stuff

Cigarettes are lit by it
Pensioners get happy when they sit by it
Fire
I like that stuff

Dankworth's alto is made of it, most of it
Scoobdedoo is composed of it
Plastic
I like that stuff

Man made fibres and raw materials
Old rolled gold and breakfast cereals
Platinum linoleum
I like that stuff

Skin on my hands
Hair on my head
Toenails on my feet
And linen on my bed

Well I like that stuff
Yes I like that stuff
The earth
Is made of earth
And I like that stuff.

ADRIAN MITCHELL

SIX LITTLE MICE

Six little mice sat down to spin;
Pussy passed by and she peeped in.
What are you doing my little men?
Weaving coats for gentlemen.
Shall I come in and cut off your threads?
No, no, mistress Pussy, you'd bite off our heads.
Oh, no, I'll not; I'll help you to spin.
That may be so, but you don't come in.

NURSERY RHYME

THE COMMON CORMORANT

The common cormorant or shag
Lays eggs inside a paper bag
The reason you will see no doubt
It is to keep the lightning out
But what these unobservant birds
Have never noticed is that herds
Of wandering bears may come with buns
And steal the bags to hold the crumbs.

ANON

THERE WAS A MAN

There was a man, he went mad,
He jumped into a paper bag;
The paper bag was too narrow,
He jumped into a wheelbarrow;
The wheelbarrow took on fire,
He jumped into a cow byre;
The cow byre was too nasty,
He jumped into an apple pasty;
The apple pasty was too sweet,
He jumped into Chester-le-Street;
Chester-le-Street was full of stones,
He fell down and broke his bones.

NURSERY RHYME

THREE YOUNG RATS

Three young rats with black felt hats,
Three young ducks with white straw flats,
Three young dogs with curling tails,
Three young cats with demi-veils,
Went out to walk with two young pigs
In satin vests and sorrel wigs;
But suddenly it chanced to rain,
And so they all went home again.

ANON

A CHARM
AGAINST THE TOOTHACHE

Venerable Mother Toothache
Climb down from your white battlements,
Stop twisting in your yellow fingers
The fourfold rope of nerves;
And tomorrow I will give you a tot of whisky
To hold in your cupped hands,
A garland of anise-flowers,
And three cloves like nails.

And tell the attendant gnomes
It is time to knock off now,
To shoulder their little pick-axes,
Their cold chisels and drills,
And you may mount by a silver ladder
Into the sky, to grind
In the cracked polished mortar
Of the hollow moon.

By the lapse of warm waters,
And the poppies nodding like red coals,
The paths on the granite mountains,
And the plantation of my dreams.

JOHN HEATH-STUBBS

BEAUTIFUL SOUP

Beautiful Soup, so rich and green,
Waiting in a hot tureen!
Who for such dainties would not stoop?
Soup of the evening, beautiful Soup!

Soup of the evening, beautiful Soup!
    Beau-ootiful Soo-oop!
    Beau-ootiful Soo-oop!
Soo-oop of the e-e-evening,
    Beautiful, beautiful Soup!

Beautiful Soup! Who cares for fish,
Game, or any other dish?
Who would not give all else for two
Pennyworth only of beautiful Soup?
Pennyworth only of beautiful Soup?
    Beau-ootiful Soo-oop!
    Beau-ootiful Soo-oop!
Soo-oop of the e-e-evening,
    Beautiful, beauti-FUL SOUP!

LEWIS CARROLL

IDENTITY PARADE

No he wasn't very *tall*
   And, no, he wasn't very *short*
He was what you'd really call
   A fairly *ordinary* sort.

No, his hair it wasn't *dark*
   But then you'd hardly call it *fair*;
Not a color you'd remark,
   Just like—well, you know, like *hair!*

Yes his suit was sort of *brown*
   Though you could have called it *gray*.
Were his cuffs turned up or down?
   Now that I'd hardly like to say.

He was not exactly *fat*
   But then I wouldn't call him *thin*.
I don't *think* his feet were flat.
   His toes turned *out*. Or was it *in!*

His tie was vivid green,
   Or, half a minute, was it blue?
Well you know just what I mean:
   It was quite a brilliant hue.

His face was somewhat red,
   Or let me think now, was it pale?
He had a heavy lightsome tread.
   Oh yes, I'm sure that he was male!

Would I know the man again?
    Do you take me for a dunce?
Out of twenty thousand men
    I'd recognize *that* man at once!

ANON

THE FOX RHYME

Aunt was on the garden seat
    Enjoying a wee nap and
Along came a fox! teeth
    Closed with a snap and
He's running to the woods with her
    A-dangle and a-flap and—
Run, uncle, run
    And see what has happened!

IAN SERRAILLIER

THE WHITE RABBIT

He is white as Helvellyn when winter is well in;
    His whiskers are mobile and tender.
If it weren't for the greed that compels him to feed
    Without ceasing, his form would be slender.

With elegant hops he crushes or crops
    All the flowers that bloom in the garden;
Yet such is the grace that suffuses his face,
    He wins, without asking, our pardon.

The sun, who rides heaven from Dover to Devon
    Inspecting furred folk and their habits,
Breaks out into poesy: "What summer snow is he
    Made of, this pearl among rabbits?"

And at night on the lawn as he waits for the dawn,
    Rapt in dreams of a rabbit's perfection,
The moon in her stride sweeps the cloudlets aside
    To rejoice in his silver reflection.

E. V. RIEU

I SAW A SHIP

I saw a ship a-sailing,
  A-sailing on the sea,
And oh but it was laden
  With pretty things for me.

There were comfits in the cabin,
  And sweetmeats in the hold;
The sails were made of silk
  And the masts were all of gold.

The four-and-twenty sailors,
  That stood between the decks,
Were four-and-twenty white mice
  With chains about their necks.

The captain was a duck
  With a jacket on his back,
And when the ship began to move
  The captain said Quack! Quack!

NURSERY RHYME

THE OWL AND THE PUSSY-CAT

The Owl and the Pussy-Cat went to sea
   In a beautiful pea-green boat,
They took some honey, and plenty of money,
   Wrapped up in a five pound note.
The Owl looked up to the stars above,
   And sang to a small guitar,
"O lovely Pussy! O Pussy my love,
   What a beautiful Pussy you are,
      You are,
      You are,
   What a beautiful Pussy you are!"

Pussy said to the Owl, "You elegant fowl!
   How charmingly sweet you sing!
O let us be married! too long have we tarried,
   But what shall we do for a ring?"
They sailed away for a year and a day,
   To the land where the Bong-tree grows,
And there in a wood a Piggy-wig stood,
   With a ring at the end of his nose,
      His nose,
      His nose,
   With a ring at the end of his nose.

"Dear Pig are you willing to sell for one shilling
   Your ring?" Said the Piggy, "I will."
So they took it away, and were married next day
   By the Turkey who lives on the hill.
They dined on mince and slices of quince,

Which they ate with a runcible spoon;
And hand in hand, on the edge of the sand,
They danced by the light of the moon,
     The moon,
     The moon,
They danced by the light of the moon.

EDWARD LEAR

THERE WAS A YOUNG FELLOW NAMED HALL

There was a young fellow named Hall,
Who fell in the spring in the fall;
     'Twould have been a sad thing
     If he'd died in the spring,
But he didn't—he died in the fall.

ANON

THE OLD MAN FROM DUNOON

There was an old man from Dunoon,
Who always ate soup with a fork,
    For he said, "As I eat
    Neither fish, fowl nor flesh,
I should finish my dinner too quick."

ANON

WILLIE'S EPITAPH

Little Willie from his mirror
    Licked the mercury right off,
Thinking, in his childish error,
    It would cure the whooping cough.
At the funeral his mother
    Smartly said to Mrs. Brown:
" 'Twas a chilly day for Willie
    When the mercury went down."

ANON

ORANGES AND LEMONS

Oranges and Lemons
Say the bells of St. Clement's.

You owe me five farthings,
Say the bells of St. Martin's.

When will you pay me?
Say the bells of Old Bailey.

When I grow rich,
Say the bells of Shoreditch.

When will that be?
Say the bells of Stepney.

I'm sure I don't know,
Says the great bell at Bow.

Here comes a candle to light you to bed,
Here comes a chopper to chop off your head.

NURSERY RHYME

A REUNION IN KENSINGTON

As I was sticking handbills on Prince Albert's prim
    anatomy
A green-faced naval colonel friend came waltzing round
    the back of me,
And since I'd often flown with him, I thought it quite
    absurd
To let him just dance on again without a single word.

I hailed him rather noisily by tweaking my suspend-
    erses
And asked if he remembered that I used to be a friend
    of his,
He said he did with ecstasy, and warmly shook my feet,
At which I offered him a half-smoked harvest-mouse
    to eat.

We hailed a sliding staircase which went up into the
    Underground.
We missed one train quite easily, but caught it as it
    turned around.
We lay down on the ceiling and, with quite undue con-
    tempt,
Tore up the blue advertisements for smell-less onion
    scent.

He said he spent his years abroad in growing sal-
    volatile,
He'd always stuck the seeds in wrong, since he pre-
    ferred philately.

He had a daughter now it seemed, and three dear little
    wives,
Who helped him making pin-cushions, and jam from
    unripe chives.

But as we talked the major shaved in a far-off pom-
    posity,
Then turning a flaming eye on me, that froze me with
    ferocity,
"You're not the man you was," he says, and slid under
    the door,
Leaving a smell of camembert and a lucky monkey's
    paw.

S. J. COHEN

TWO OR THREE

Two or three Posies
With two or three simples—
Two or three Noses
With two or three pimples—
Two or three wise men
And two or three ninnies—
Two or three purses
And two or three guineas—
Two or three raps
At two or three doors—
Two or three naps
Of two or three hours—
Two or three Cats
And two or three mice—
Two or three sprats
At a very great price—
Two or three sandies
And two or three tabbies—
Two or three dandies
And two Mrs. Abbeys
Two or three Smiles
And two or three frowns—
Two or three Miles
To two or three towns—
Two or three pegs
For two or three bonnets—
Two or three dove eggs
To hatch into sonnets.

JOHN KEATS

JIM JAY

Do diddle di do,
   Poor Jim Jay
Got stuck fast
   In Yesterday.
Squinting he was,
   On cross-legs bent,
Never heeding
   The wind was spent.
Round veered the weathercock,
   The sun drew in—
And stuck was Jim
   Like a rusty pin. . . .
We pulled and we pulled
   From seven till twelve,
Jim too frightened
   To help himself.
But all in vain.
   The clock struck one,
And there was Jim
   A little bit gone.
At half-past five
   You scarce could see
A glimpse of his flapping
   Handkerchee.
And when came noon,
   And we climbed sky-high,
Jim was a speck
   Slip—slipping by.
Come tomorrow
   The neighbours say,
He'll be past crying for:
   Poor Jim Jay.

WALTER DE LA MARE

WHAT BECAME OF THEM?

He was a rat, and she was a rat,
   And down in one hole they did dwell,
And both were as black as a witch's cat,
   And they loved one another well.

He had a tail, and she had a tail,
   Both long and curling and fine;
And each said, "Yours is the finest tail
   In the world, excepting mine."

He smelt the cheese, and she smelt the cheese,
   And they both pronounced it good;
And both remarked it would greatly add
   To the charms of their daily food.

So he ventured out, and she ventured out,
   And I saw them go with pain;
But what befell them I never can tell,
   For they never came back again.

ANON

WISDOMS, PRAISE, PRAYERS AND GRACES

O MANY NAMED BELOVED

O Many Named Beloved
Listen to my praise
Various as the seasons
Different as the days
All my treasons cease
When I see your face.

SAMUEL MENASHE

WITH FLOWERS

I've nothing else to bring, you know,
So I keep bringing these—
Just as the night keeps fetching stars
To our familiar eyes.
Maybe we shouldn't mind them
Unless they didn't come—
Then maybe it would puzzle us
To find our way home.

EMILY DICKINSON

UPON A CHILD

Here a pretty baby lies
Sung asleep with lullabies;
Pray be silent, and do not stir
The easy earth that covers her.

ROBERT HERRICK

EVERYONE SANG

Everyone suddenly burst out singing;
And I was filled with such delight
As prisoned birds must find in freedom
Winging wildly across the white
Orchards and dark green fields; on; on; and out of sight.

Everyone's voice was suddenly lifted,
And beauty came like the setting sun,
My heart was shaken with tears and horror
Drifted away . . . O but every one
Was a bird; and the song was wordless; the singing will
　　never be done.

SIEGFRIED SASSOON

DAYS

What are days for?
Days are where we live.
They come, they wake us
Time and time over.
They are to be happy in:
Where can we live but days?

Ah, solving that question
Brings the priest and the doctor
In their long coats
Running over the fields.

PHILIP LARKIN

ADIEU

Here are some flowers to remember me by
In just a day or two they'll die
I wouldn't ask to be remembered long
If I did I'd give you a stone.

PAUL LEWENSTEIN

GOD BE IN MY HEAD

God be in my head
And in my understanding;
God be in mine eyes,
And in my looking;
God be in my mouth,
And in my speaking;
God be in my heart,
And in my thinking;
God be at my end and at my departing.

ANON

NOW I LAY ME DOWN TO SLEEP

Now I lay me down to sleep
I pray the Lord my soul to keep;
And if I die before I wake,
I pray the Lord my soul to take.

NURSERY RHYME

OH LADY

Oh Lady lonely as a stone—
Even here moss has grown

SAMUEL MENASHE

213

RUMINATION

When I can hold a stone within my hand
And feel time make it sand and soil, and see
The roots of living things grow in this land,
Pushing between my fingers flower and tree,
Then I shall be as wise as death,
For death has done this and he will
Do this to me, and blow his breath
To fire my clay, when I am still.

RICHARD EBERHART

SONG OF A HEBREW

Working is another way of praying.
You plant in Israel the soul of a tree.
You plant in the desert the spirit of gardens.

Praying is another way of singing.
You plant in the tree the soul of lemons.
You plant in the gardens the spirit of roses.

Singing is another way of loving.
You plant in the lemons the spirit of your son.
You plant in the roses the soul of your daughter.

Loving is another way of living.
You plant in your daughter the spirit of Israel.
You plant in your son the soul of the desert.

DANNIE ABSE

BAPTIST

The water
of the world
is love

The Water
of the World
is Love

SAMUEL MENASHE

I SEE THE MOON

I see the moon
   And the moon sees me;
God bless the moon,
   And God bless me.

NURSERY RHYME

GRACE FOR A CHILD

Here a little child I stand,
Heaving up my either hand;
Cold as paddocks though they be,
Here I lift them up to Thee;
For a benison to fall
On our meat, and on us all.

ROBERT HERRICK

GOLDEN SLUMBERS

Golden slumbers kiss your eyes,
Smiles awake you when you rise.
Sleep, pretty wantons, do not cry,
And I will sing a lullaby:
Rock them, rock them, lullaby.

Care is heavy, therefore sleep you;
You are care, and care must keep you.
Sleep, pretty wantons, do not cry,
And I will sing a lullaby:
Rock them, rock them, lullaby.

THOMAS DEKKER

REQUIEM

Under the wide and starry sky
Dig the grave and let me lie.
Glad did I live and gladly die,
And I laid me down with a will.

This be the verse you grave for me:
Here he lies where he longed to be:
Home is the sailor, home from sea,
And the hunter home from the hill.

ROBERT LOUIS STEVENSON

CANDLES

The days of our future stand before us
Like a row of little lighted candles—
golden, warm, and lively little candles.

The days gone by remain behind us,
a mournful line of burnt-out candles;
the nearest ones are still smoking,
cold candles, melted and bent.

I do not want to look at them; their form saddens me,
and it saddens me to recall their first light.
I look ahead at my lighted candles.

I do not want to turn back, lest I see and shudder—
how quickly the sombre line lengthens,
how quickly the burnt-out candles multiply.

C. P. CAVAFY
(*translated by Rae Dalven*)

FOR SLEEP, OR DEATH

Cure me with quietness,
Bless me with peace;
Comfort my heaviness,
Stay me with ease.
Stillness in solitude
Send down like dew;
Mine armour of fortitude
Piece and make new:
That when I rise again
I may shine bright
As the sky after rain,
Day after night.

RUTH PITTER

REVELATION

At the midnight of the year
I saw them suddenly appear,
Ranks of angels in the sky.
In order they began the cry
Of "Magnify, O magnify"
Above a shabby, northern street
Until their concord was complete.
But still the town's black work went on
Though over it all heaven shone,
Though every cobble was ablaze
And gutters running songs of praise.

LEONARD CLARK

THE CAROL OF
THE POOR CHILDREN

We are the poor children, come out to see the sights
On this day of all days, on this night of nights,
The stars in merry parties are dancing in the sky,
A fine star, a new star, is shining on high!

We are the poor children, our lips are frosty blue,
We cannot sing our carol as well as rich folk do,
Our bellies are so empty we have no singing voice,
But this night of all nights good children must rejoice.

We do rejoice, we do rejoice, as hard as we can try,
A fine star, a new star is shining in the sky!
And while we sing our carol, we think of the delight
The happy kings and shepherds make in Bethlehem to-
    night.

Are we naked, mother, and are we starving-poor—
Oh, see what gifts the kings have brought outside the
    stable door,
Are we cold, mother, the ass will give his hay
To make the manger warm and keep the cruel winds
    away.

We are the poor children, but not so poor who sing
Our carol with our voiceless hearts to greet the new-
    born king,
On this night of all nights, when in the frosty sky
A new star, a kind star is shining on high!

RICHARD MIDDLETON

from *AUGURIES OF INNOCENCE*

To see a World in a Grain of Sand
And a Heaven in a Wild Flower,
Hold Infinity in the palm of your hand
And Eternity in an hour.

A Robin Red breast in a Cage
Puts all Heaven in a Rage.
A dove house fill'd with doves & Pigeons
Shudders Hell thro' all its regions.
A dog starv'd at his Master's Gate
Predicts the ruin of the State.
A Horse misus'd upon the Road
Calls to Heaven for Human blood.
Each outcry of the hunted Hare
A fibre from the Brain does tear.
A Skylark wounded in the wing,
A Cherubim does cease to sing.
The Game Cock clip'd & arm'd for fight
Does the Rising Sun affright.
Every Wolf's & Lion's howl
Raises from Hell a Human Soul.
The wild deer, wand'ring here and there,
Keeps the Human Soul from Care.
The Lamb misus'd breeds Public strife
And yet forgives the Butcher's Knife.
The Bat that flits at close of Eve
Has left the Brain that won't Believe.
The Owl that calls upon the Night
Speaks the Unbeliever's fright.
He who shall hurt the little Wren
Shall never be belov'd by Men.
He who the Ox to wrath has mov'd

Shall never be by Woman lov'd.
The wanton Boy that kills the Fly
Shall feel the Spider's enmity.
He who torments the Chafer's sprite
Weaves a Bower in endless Night.
The Caterpillar on the Leaf
Repeats to thee thy Mother's grief.
Kill not the Moth nor Butterfly,
For the Last Judgment draweth nigh.
He who shall train the Horse to War
Shall never pass the Polar Bar.
The Beggar's Dog & Widow's Cat,
Feed them and thou wilt grow fat.

WILLIAM BLAKE

IN THE FIELDS

Lord, when I look at lovely things which pass,
   Under old trees the shadows of young leaves
Dancing to please the wind along the grass,
    Or the gold stillness of the August sun on the August
      sheaves;
Can I believe there is a heavenlier world than this?
   And if there is
Will the strange heart of any everlasting thing
   Bring me these dreams that take my breath away?
They come at evening with the home-flying rooks and
     the scent of hay,
   Over the fields. They come in Spring.

CHARLOTTE MEW

PIED BEAUTY

Glory be to God for dappled things—
 For skies of couple-colour as a brinded cow;
  For rose-moles all in stipple upon trout that swim;
Fresh-firecoal chestnut-falls; finches' wings;
 Landscape plotted and pieced—fold, fallow, and
   plough;
  And all trades, their gear and tackle and trim.

All things counter, original, spare, strange;
 Whatever is fickle, freckled (who knows how?)
  With swift, slow; sweet, sour; adazzle, dim;
He fathers-forth whose beauty is past change:
   Praise him.

GERARD MANLEY HOPKINS

BURY HER AT EVEN

Bury her at even
That the stars may shine
Soon above her,
And the dews of twilight cover:
Bury her at even
Ye that love her.

Bury her at even
In the wind's decline;
Night receive her
Where no noise can ever grieve her!
Bury her at even,
And then leave her!

MICHAEL FIELD

NAME OR PERSON

Your name or your person
Which is dearer?
Your person or your goods
Which is worth more?
Gain or loss,
Which is the greater bane?
That is why excessive meanness
Is sure to lead to great expense;
Too much store
Is sure to end in immense loss.
Know contentment
And you will suffer no disgrace;
Know when to stop
And you will meet with no danger.
You can then endure.

LAO TZU

(translated by D. C. Lau)

QUESTIONS OF
A STUDIOUS WORKING MAN

Who built Thebes of the seven gates?
In the books you find the names of kings.
Was it the kings who hauled chunks of rock to the
    place?
And Babylon, many times demolished,
Who raised it up again so many times? In what houses
Of gold-glittering Lima did the builders live?
Where, the evening that the Great Wall of China was
    finished,
Did the masons go? Great Rome
Is full of triumphal arches. Over whom
Did the Caesars triumph? Had Byzantium, much
    praised in song,
Only palaces for its inhabitants? Even in fabulous
    Atlantis,
The very night the ocean engulfed it,
The drowning still roared for their slaves.
Young Alexander conquered India.
Was it he alone?
Caesar defeated the Gauls.
Did he not have a cook at least in his service?
Philip of Spain wept when his armada
Had sunk. Was he the only one to weep?
Frederick the Second won the Seven Years' War. Who
Else won that war?

Every page a victory.
Who cooked the feast for the victors?

Every ten years a great man.
Who paid the bill?

So many accounts
So many questions.

BERTOLT BRECHT
(*translated by Yvonne Kapp*)

Song from *THE PRINCESS*

Sweet and low, sweet and low,
   Wind of the western sea,
Low, low, breathe and blow,
Wind of the western sea!
Over the rolling waters go,
Come from the dying moon, and blow,
   Blow him again to me;
While my little one, while my pretty one, sleeps.

Sleep and rest, sleep and rest,
   Father will come to thee soon;
Rest, rest on mother's breast,
   Father will come to thee soon;
Father will come to his babe in the nest,
Silver sails all out of the west
   Under the silver moon:
Sleep, my little one, sleep, my pretty one, sleep.

ALFRED, LORD TENNYSON

NURSE'S SONG

Sleep, baby, sleep!
Your father herds his sheep:
Your mother shakes the little tree
From which fall pretty dreams on thee;
Sleep, baby, sleep!

Sleep, baby, sleep!
The heavens are white with sheep:
For they are lambs—those stars so bright:
And the moon's shepherd of the night;
Sleep, baby, sleep!

Sleep, baby, sleep!
And I'll give thee a sheep,
Which, with its golden bell, shall be
A little play-fellow for thee;
Sleep, baby, sleep!

Sleep, baby, sleep!
And bleat not like a sheep,
Or else the shepherd's angry dog
Will come and bite my naughty rogue;
Sleep, baby, sleep!

Sleep, baby, sleep!
Go out and herd the sheep,
Go out, you barking black dog, go,
And waken not my baby so;
Sleep, baby, sleep!

ANON
(*translated from the German*)

AS I SAT UNDER A SYCAMORE TREE

As I sat under a sycamore tree,
  A sycamore tree, a sycamore tree,
I looked me out upon the sea
  On Christ's Sunday at morn.

I saw three ships a-sailing there,
  A-sailing there, a-sailing there,
Jesu, Mary and Joseph they bare
  On Christ's Sunday at morn.

Joseph did whistle and Mary did sing,
  Mary did sing, Mary did sing,
And all the bells on Earth did ring
  For joy our Lord was born.

O they sailed into Bethlehem,
  To Bethlehem, to Bethlehem;
St. Michael was the sterësman,
  St. John sat in the horn.

And all the bells on earth did ring,
  On earth did ring, on earth did ring:
"Welcome be thou Heaven's King,
  On Christ's Sunday at morn!"

ANON

MIRACLES

Why, who makes much of a miracle?
As to me I know of nothing else but miracles,
Whether I walk in the streets of Manhattan,
Or dart my sight over the roofs of houses toward the
     sky,
Or wade with naked feet along the beach just in the
     edge of the water
Or stand under trees in the woods,
Or talk by day with any one I love,
Or sleep in the bed at night with any one I love,
Or sit at table at dinner with the rest,
Or look at strangers opposite me riding in the car,
Or watch honey-bees busy around the hive of a summer
     forenoon,
Or animals feeding in the fields,
Or birds, or the wonderfulness of insects in the air,
Or the wonderfulness of the sundown, or of stars
     shining so quiet and bright,
Or the exquisite delicate thin curve of the new moon
     in spring;
Those with the rest, one and all, are to me miracles,
The whole referring, yet each distinct in its place.
To me every hour of the light and dark is a miracle,
Every cubic inch of space is a miracle,
Every square yard of the surface of the earth is spread
     with the same,
Every foot of the interior swarms with the same.

To me the sea is a continual miracle,
The fishes that swim—the rocks—the motion of the
waves—the ships with men in them.
What stranger miracles are there?

WALT WHITMAN

STONE TOO CAN PRAY

Lord, Lord,—these miracles, the streets, all say,—
bring to us soon thy best most golden day,
that every stick and stone for thee may shine,
thy praise be sung in every shaft and line.

Lord, Lord,—the steeples and the towers cry,—
deepen beyond belief this ancient sky,
darker than time, or terror, be that blue,
and we'll still praise thee by still pointing true.

Lord, Lord,—the fountains weep,—hear our delight,
these waters for birds and children we keep bright,
where children shout, and the stone dolphin sings,
thy rainbow blessed by holy eyes and wings.

Lord, Lord, all voices say, and all together,
stone, steel, and waking man and waking weather,
give us thy day, that once more we may be
the endless miracle that embodies thee.

CONRAD AIKEN

NOTES ON THE POEMS

THE NORTH WIND DOTH BLOW (page 2)
> The text of this and the other nursery rhymes in the book is taken from *The Oxford Nursery Rhyme Book,* edited by Iona and Peter Opie.

HAREBELL (page 2)
> Written during the Second World War when the author was a prisoner of war in Germany.

PUSSY AT THE FIRESIDE (page 4)
> "Pease brose"=pease porridge.

CHILD'S SONG (page 9)
> Siha is *Psoralea plicata,* a Middle Eastern plant resembling a very luxurious everlasting sweet pea.

SUNDAY AT HAMPSTEAD (page 12)
> The initials "B.V." stand for Bysshe Vanolis. The author was a great admirer of Percy Bysshe Shelley and of Novalis, and he used this anagram as a pseudonym to help distinguish him from James Thompson, author of *The Seasons.*

CAST OUR CAPS AND CARES AWAY (page 17)
> "Sessed"=assessed. The beggars cannot be assessed and taxed on their wealth because they have none.

IN MARBLE HALLS (page 32)
> This is a riddle. The answer is—an egg.

THE FALCON (page 36)
> I have changed the spelling which is normally "faucon." "Make" =mate.

A MEETING (page 40)
> A complete section of a poem in three parts dealing with meetings with a double or doppelganger.

LA BELLE DAME SANS MERCI (page 46)
> Keats originally wrote "Knight at Arms" but changed this to "wretched wight." As is usual in modern practice I have preferred "Knight at Arms," which does not have about it the peculiarly dated air of "wight."

CORTEZ (page 64)
> Cortez (1485-1547) was the conqueror of Mexico.

THE BALLAD OF THE OYSTERMAN (page 69)
> This is a satirical gloss on the classical tale of the love of Leander

for Hero. Hero was the priestess of Venus at Sestos, and Leander swam the Hellespont from Abydos every evening to see her until, one winter night, he was drowned.

THE AKOND OF SWAT (page 100)
Edward Lear has this note at the foot of the poem: "For the existence of this potentate see Indian newspapers, *passim*. The proper way to read the verses is to make an immense emphasis on the monosyllabic rhymes which indeed ought to be shouted out by a chorus."

ALBERT (page 109)
Abelard and Heloise were two of the great lovers in history, as well as being remarkable writers and personages. He became a priest and she became a nun.

TIMOTHY WINTERS (page 123)
"Helves"=plead or entreat (a Cornish word).

A SONG ABOUT MYSELF (page 131)
A squib included in a letter to Fanny. Not one of Keats' poems proper.

GAY COMES THE SINGER (page 142)
A poem from one of the great collections of medieval Latin verse.

BIRDS MUST SING (page 152)
"Brume"=a thin shifting fog.

TAILOR'S SONG (page 178)
"Hunter"—the image is taken from the kind of watch which has a metal case (usually made of gold) to protect the glass, and which is carried in a man's waistcoat pocket. "Singer"=sewing machine.

STUFF (page 190)
Johnnie Dankworth—the famous saxophone player.

THE WHITE RABBIT (page 198)
Helvellyn—a mountain in Westmorland.

TWO OR THREE (page 206)
This is taken from a letter of Keats' sister. Line 20 actually reads: "And two Mrs. . . . Mum!" but I have supplied the name Abbey rather than relegate it to a footnote.

BURY HER AT EVEN (page 222)
Michael Field was the name taken by two women poets: Katherine Bradley and Edith Cooper.

NAME OR PERSON (page 223)
A fragment from the great Chinese philosophical work *Tao Te Ching*.

INDEX TO AUTHORS

INDEX TO FIRST LINES